HOWARD R. BOWEN, Chairman of the National Commission on Technology, Automation, and Economic Progress and President of the University of Iowa, is also the author of *Social Responsibilities of the Businessman, Toward Social Economy, Graduate Education in Economics,* and several other books and articles.

GARTH L. MANGUM, Executive Secretary of the National Commission on Technology, Automation, and Economic Progress and Director, Manpower Policy Evaluation Project, W. E. Upjohn Institute for Employment Research, is also the author of *The Operating Engineers: Economic History of a Trade Union,* editor of *The Manpower Revolution: Its Policy Consequences,* and is the author of several other books and articles.

AUTOMATION

AND ECONOMIC

PROGRESS

AUTOMATION

AND ECONOMIC

PROGRESS

Edited by

Howard R. Bowen and *Garth L. Mangum*

Prentice-Hall, Inc.   A SPECTRUM BOOK   *Englewood, Cliffs, N.J.*

Current printing (last number):
10 9 8 7 6 5 4 3 2 1

Table of Contents

SELECTIONS FROM SUPPLEMENTARY STUDIES

THE OUTLOOK FOR TECHNOLOGICAL CHANGE AND EMPLOYMENT

THE PACE OF TECHNOLOGICAL CHANGE

EMPLOYMENT IMPACT OF TECHNOLOGICAL CHANGE

ADJUSTING TO CHANGE

AUTOMATION

AND ECONOMIC

PROGRESS

Technology and the American Economy: Condensation of the Report

EDITORS' INTRODUCTION

During the years following the Korean conflict, unemployment crept persistently upward. The unemployment level rose and fell with the business cycle, but at each peak and trough it stood at higher levels than during the cycle before. Then it lodged at above 5 per cent and stuck there, despite what seemed to be strenuous attempts to lower it through area redevelopment and manpower training measures.

The causes of persistent unemployment became a major public policy issue, with opinion divided between those who saw the problem as one of "round pegs and square holes"—structural unemployment—and those who blamed a deficiency of aggregate demand. A third hypothesis, held by many in both the structural and aggregative camps, placed major blame on technological change, especially automation.

"Automation" is a catchy term. Technically, it means the application of electronic controls, including self-adjusting feedback mechanisms, to mechanical production processes. In common parlance it became synonymous with any force having a negative effect upon employment. Essentially, three questions were involved in speculations about the role of automation in unemployment:

1. Had the pace of technological change accelerated until the economy could no longer make adequate adjustments?
2. Was technological change a major cause of persistently high general levels of unemployment?
3. Was the new technology so twisting the demand for labor that the under-educated and unskilled were becoming unemployable while the demands for highly trained manpower were insatiable?

Major labor-management disputes in the railroad, airline, steel, meat-

1

packing, longshoring, and maritime industries involved issues of adjustment to technological change. In the summer of 1963, confronted by the threat of a nationwide railroad strike involving such technological issues, President John F. Kennedy sent to Congress a message requesting passage of a compulsory arbitration law tailored to that particular dispute. In his message President Kennedy promised to establish a presidential commission to determine the impact of automation and technological change on the economy. The result was passage on August 14, 1964, over a year later, of Public Law 88–444, calling upon President Johnson to appoint a fourteen-member National Commission on Technology, Automation, and Economic Progress.

In the interim another series of issues had been added. In the fall of 1963 defense expenditures, which had grown rapidly during the previous two years, began to slow their rate of increase. At the same time a shift from missile and space-oriented defense expenditures to more conventional arms was beginning. The economic impact of defense and disarmament became a major issue. What should be done with the released resources? Why not use the same skills which could put men into orbit and make lunar landings appear practical to heal the ills of the earthly environment—traffic congestion, dilapidated housing, air and water pollution, inadequate education and health care—which had accumulated through urbanization and population growth during years of preoccupation with depressions and hot and cold wars?

The mandate of the Commission reflected both concerns:

1. to identify and assess the past effects and the current and prospective role and pace of technological change;
2. to identify and describe the impact of technological and economic change on production and employment, including new job requirements and the major types of worker displacement, both technological and economic, which are likely to occur during the next ten years; the specific industries, occupations, and geographic areas which are most likely to be involved; and the social and economic effects of these developments on the nation's economy, manpower, communities, families, social structure, and human values;
3. to define those areas of unmet community and human needs toward which application of new technologies might most effectively be directed, encompassing an examination of technological developments that have occurred in recent years, including those resulting from the federal government's research and development programs;
4. to assess the most effective means for channeling new technologies into promising directions, including civilian industries where accelerated technological advancements will yield general benefits, and the proper relationship between governmental and private investment in the application of new technologies to large-scale human and community needs;
5. to recommend, in addition to those actions which are the responsibility

of management and labor, specific administrative and legislative steps which it believes should be taken by the federal, state, and local governments in meeting their responsibilities (a) to support and promote technological change in the interest of continued economic growth and improved well-being of our people, (b) to continue and adopt measures which will facilitate occupational adjustment and geographical mobility, and (c) to share the costs and help prevent and alleviate the adverse impact of change on displaced workers.

There was more pressing business in the political world in the fall of 1964 than the appointment of commissions. January 1965 arrived before the members of the National Commission on Technology, Automation, and Economic Progress were nominated and approved by the Senate. The members were:

Dr. Howard R. Bowen, President, University of Iowa, *Chairman*
Mr. Benjamin Aaron, Professor of Law and Director, Institute of Industrial Relations, University of California at Los Angeles
Mr. Joseph A. Beirne, President, Communications Workers of America
Dr. Daniel Bell, Chairman, Sociology Department, Columbia University
Mr. Patrick E. Haggerty, President, Texas Instruments, Incorporated
Mr. Albert J. Hayes, Past President, International Association of Machinists
Mrs. Anna Rosenberg Hoffman, President, Anna M. Rosenberg Associates
Dr. Edwin H. Land, President and Research Director, Polaroid Corporation
Mr. Walter P. Reuther, President, United Automobile Workers
Mr. Robert H. Ryan, President, Regional Industrial Development Corporation of Southwestern Pennsylvania
Dr. Robert M. Solow, Professor of Economics, Massachusetts Institute of Technology
Mr. Philip Sporn, Chairman, System Development Committee, American Electric Power Company
Mr. Thomas J. Watson, Jr., Chairman of the Board, IBM Corporation[1]
Mr. Whitney M. Young, Jr., Executive Director, National Urban League

The Commission met for the first time in late January 1965 and continued meeting through January 1966. The timing had particular significance: in July 1963 unemployment was 5.6 per cent; in August 1964 it was 5.1 per cent; in January 1965 it was 4.8 per cent; by January 1966 it had fallen to 4.1 per cent. Unemployment had been the reason for the Commission's creation; during the Commission's deliberations the economy was answering the three basic questions with a resounding, "No!" The pace of technological change had indeed accelerated, but it was still well within the reach of economic growth rates attainable through well known fiscal and monetary policies. The high general levels of unemployment had been caused by slow economic growth resulting

[1]Appointed July 31, 1965, following the death of John L. Snyder, Jr.

from passive fiscal policies, not by technological change. Employers would employ the educated and skilled before the uneducated and unskilled, but, given adequate demand for their products, they would dip into whatever labor pools were available.

The Commission held that adequate economic growth through aggressive fiscal and monetary policy was "not the end of economic policy, but it was the beginning." Technological change was recognized as only one of many kinds of change causing the displacement of particular persons in particular establishments, occupations, industries, and localities. But displacement became manageable only when other jobs were available to absorb the displaced and new entrants to the labor force. Any displacement was painful, but the real tragedies were (1) displacement in slack labor markets, and (2) displacement of those cut off from access to other employment opportunities by geography and lack of education and transferable skills. Coal miners and agricultural workers were the prime examples of the latter.

The Commission chose to view the labor market as a "gigantic shape-up" with available workers queued up in order of their relative attractiveness to employers. The attractiveness might be determined by rational criteria such as skill and education or by the irrationality of prejudice. To get the employer to reach more deeply down the line, it was only necessary to increase the demand for his goods and services. But no matter how deeply the employer reached, left over at the back of the line were still those with the greatest disadvantages in the competition for jobs. The economic demand necessary to force the employer to reach clear to the back of the line would ultimately lead to unacceptable price level increases (though the Commission was unwilling to accept 4 per cent or even 3 per cent unemployment as a stopping place). The individual employer, after all, had an alternative. He could bid for the services of the more attractive workers already employed, and neither businessmen nor labor organizations were likely to ignore their opportunities to exploit a seller's market.

However, those at the back of the line, the Commission thought, need not be abandoned to unemployment. The Commission chose to take seriously the phrase in the Employment Act of 1946 promising "useful employment opportunities for all those able, willing, and seeking to work." Education and training could increase the ability of those at the back of the queue to compete with those nearer the front. Better employment services and relocation assistance could speed and improve man-job matches. Employers and unions could agree on measures to facilitate the adjustment to change. But this would not be enough.

The Commission was struck, as many people have been, with the incongruity of involuntary idleness while so many useful tasks remained undone. The workings of a private enterprise economy seemed capable, given adequate purchasing power, of producing the goods and services needed to fill private demand, but production for public consumption was notably inadequate. Therefore, the Commission charged the federal government to become "the employer of last resort," providing useful public service employment for all those not absorbed by the private profit-making sectors of the economy.

The Commission was also concerned with the substantial numbers who could never even get into the lineup—families without a bread-winner. Therefore, the Commission recommended that a floor be placed under family incomes, guaranteeing an adequate minimum income allowance to all, yet maintaining incentive to move upward to higher incomes where employability existed.

The Commission has been accused of inconsistency, taking a sanguine view of the employment impact of technological change, then recommending radical solutions to supposedly nonexistent problems. Were the Commission still in existence, it would probably reply, "We said, 'don't worry about automation.' We didn't say, 'don't worry.'" General unemployment is no less real and less painful just because it is not the result of technological change. Particular unemployment can occur from technological as well as other changes. To the displaced employee, it is immaterial whether demand for his employer's product declined, his employer went out of business or relocated, or his job was taken by an electronic gadget. "Displacement is the price of a dynamic economy," the Commission said. The burdens and benefits must be distributed fairly, both as a matter of equity and because, in a political and industrial democracy, threatened individuals and institutions will resist change, regardless of its promise for the general welfare.

The Commission considered the potential benefits as well as the threats of technological change. It saw that advancing productivity could open new options at a rate doubling the output of an hour's work every quarter century. The productivity could be taken in higher incomes, greater leisure, improvements in work environment, public investment in the quality of American life, or assistance to less advantaged countries.

Many human and community needs remain unmet. Space and defense efforts have demonstrated impressively our technological ability to attack and solve complex problems. What are the obstacles to similar accomplishment in solving the problems of the terrestrial environment? The Commission chose from among the numerous social problems amenable, at least in part, to technological solutions, health care, urban transportation, housing, and air and water pollution. Using these as examples, it explored some of the institutional obstacles. The problem, it decided, lay primarily in the decision-making mechanisms. There were technological obstacles, but where we had put our minds and resources to the task, they had been removed. On the goals of defense and space there was a consensus. An equal consensus on social goals required better means of displaying the alternatives, measuring the costs and benefits, and agreeing upon the goals and procedures. Improvements in these decision-making mechanisms absorbed the final third of the Commission report.

The degree of accord among fourteen people of diverse affiliations was remarkable. Each individual had and exercised the right to disassociate himself from any finding or recommendation with which he did not agree. Though these comments have been deleted from the condensation of the report which follows, the point at which they appeared and the names of the dissenting members are given. The equal number of cases in which individuals wanted to go beyond the Commission's recommendations are not noted in the condensation. The full range of opinion was indicated by the first two footnote comments in the report. Five members, including the three labor representatives, "concurred with the analysis and recommendations" but thought the report missed an appropriate "tone of urgency." They were confident of the economic solvability of the problems but not of the nation's political will. This comment was followed by one from two industry members, also endorsing the findings and recommendations but rapping the lack of "adequate emphasis on the positive contributions."

Beyond these comments, there were dissents from such recommendations as federalizing the state employment services, but on the seemingly more radical proposals—the government as "employer of last resort" and the guaranteed family income—there was complete consensus throughout the deliberations. The Commission was publicized as divided at one point, but the major bone of contention was the labor movement's commitment to shorter hours of work, an obstacle which was removed by ignoring the issue.

Concern for unemployment was declining as the Commission deliberated. The first of seven drafts, written in July 1965, contained a carefully worked out fiscal program to bring unemployment to 4 per cent by January 1967 and 3 per cent by January 1968. The proposal was revised and finally dropped. Instead of providing answers to intransigent general unemployment, the report recommended seemingly radical new programs to aid the competitively disadvantaged at a time when the maintenance of the existing commitment was in doubt.

With foreign military involvements absorbing priority policy attention, the Commission's report met with complete silence from the administration and Congress. The response outside of government was more heartening—not necessarily approving, but attentive. Those who put so much of themselves into the report are grateful for anything that keeps their recommendations alive until the competition for public attention diminishes. Not that the Commission ever thought of itself as making policy, but the members did have hopes of at least giving policy a shove in what they considered to be the right direction.

The Commission's report, entitled *Technology and the American Economy*, is 115 pages long. The Commission did not depend upon its own knowledge and experience alone. It invited various knowledgeable people for informal discussions; it addressed a general invitation to individuals, companies, unions, and trade associations to submit statements relevant to the Commission's mandate; it funded forty-one studies in which it asked individual experts, government agencies, and research organizations to define the issues and summarize the literature and past research in a particular field, to undertake original research, and to offer independent judgments based on study and experience. The Commission studied these supplementary documents, accepting some recommendations and rejecting others but absorbing the facts from all. Then, because the Commission considered them of value, it published them in six volumes.

One of the drawbacks of government documents is their bulk and the lack of a distribution system. It was with enthusiasm, therefore, that the Commission's Chairman and Executive Secretary reacted to an invitation from Prentice-Hall, Inc., to publish a condensation of the report and selections from the supplementary studies. The condensing was done, for the most part, by Mr. Francis Bello, Associate Editor of *Scientific American*. It follows the text faithfully, but with deletion of explanatory and sometimes qualifying material, bringing the report to one third its original length. Space limitations made it necessary to select within as well as among the forty-one studies. The ten from which selections were chosen are those which seemed to be most attractive to the general reader yet representative of the Commission's range of interests. Deletions from the studies are not noted. Where necessary to bridge extracts, words have been inserted which were not in the original text. Care has been taken not to bias the original context, but any failure to preserve original meanings and nuances is our responsibility, not that of the original author.

I.   THE PACE OF TECHNOLOGICAL CHANGE

It has become a commonplace that the world is experiencing a scientific and technological revolution. Stock phrases—"knowledge revolution," "second industrial revolution," "automation revolution"—express this belief. According to one extreme view, the world, or at least the United States, is on the verge of a glut of productivity sufficient to make our economic institutions and the notion of gainful employment obsolete. The Commission dissents from this view. We believe that the evidence does not support it, and that it diverts attention from the real problems of our country and the world. We also dissent, however, from the other extreme view of complacency that denies the existence of serious social and economic problems related to the impact of technological change.

Our study of the evidence has impressed us with the inadequacy of the basis for any sweeping pronouncements about the speed of scientific and technological progress. One can, however, reach certain reasonable judgments. Our broad conclusion is that the pace of technological change has increased in recent decades and may increase in the future, but a sharp break in the continuity of technical progress has not occurred, nor is it likely to occur in the next decade.

There is no direct way to measure the number of significant technological innovations or their economic effects. In the absence of such measures, indirect ones must do. The most useful are indexes of productivity and productivity growth, particularly output per man-hour (the volume of final output of goods and services produced in a year divided by the number of man-hours worked in the year.)

In the thirty-five years before the end of the Second World War, output per man-hour in the private economy rose at a trend rate of 2 per cent a year. But for the Depression of the 1930s, the rate might have been higher. Between 1947 and 1965 productivity in the private economy rose at a trend rate of about 3.2 per cent a year. (See Figure 1.) If agriculture is excluded, the contrast is less sharp: a rate of increase of 2 per cent a year before the war and 2.5 per cent after it. For manufacturing industries alone, the postwar rate of productivity gain was 2.6 per cent a year.

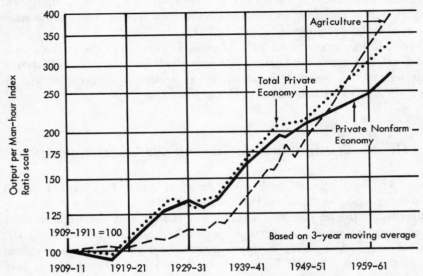

SOURCE: Unless otherwise indicated, all charts are compiled from information provided by the U. S. Department of Commerce and Bureau of Labor Statistics, U. S. Department of Labor.

Figure 1. Indexes of Output per Man Hour: Total Private Farm and Private Nonfarm Economy, 1909-65

If this increase in the rate of productivity growth does not square with the assumption that a veritable technological revolution has occurred, the increase is nevertheless substantial. Anything growing at 2 per cent a year doubles in thirty-six years; anything growing at 2.5 per cent a year doubles in twenty-eight years; anything growing at 3 per cent a year doubles in about twenty-four years. When the product of an hour of work doubles in only twenty-four years—not much more than half a working lifetime—it is hardly surprising that people should feel that their environment is in continuous flux.

One other aspect of innovation is partially amenable to measurement: the time elapsed between the birth of a new scientific or technical idea and its commercial application or acceptance. Studies made for the Commission indicate that the time elapsed between technical discovery and commercial recognition fell from about thirty years before the First World War to sixteen years between the wars, and to nine years after the Second World War. The additional time required to convert these technical discoveries to initial commercial application has decreased from about seven to about five years. Nevertheless, it seems safe to conclude that most technological discoveries which will have a significant impact within the next decade are already in a readily identifiable stage of commercial development.

We find, in summary, evidence of enough increase in the pace of technological and economic change to remove any ground for complacency. Our society has not met the challenge of technical progress with complete success. There is much to be done.

II.   Technological Change and Unemployment

The language and legislative history of Public Law 88–444, which established this Commission, leave no doubt that Congress was seriously concerned with the role of technological change and the high level of unemployment which persisted in the United States after 1953. At the end of the Korean War, unemployment began to creep upward from an average level of some 3 per cent of the civilian labor force; it rose and fell with economic conditions, but stalled at higher levels at the peak of each succeeding business cycle, finally reaching a high point of 7.1 per cent in May 1961. The explanation was sought by some in the dramatic technological changes that had occurred during the 1950s.

We believe that the general level of unemployment must be distinguished from the displacement of particular workers at particular times and places if the relation between technological change and unemployment is to be clearly understood. The persistence of a high general level of unemployment in the years following the Korean War was not the result of accelerated technological progress. Its cause was interaction between rising productivity, labor force growth, and an inadequate growth of aggregate demand. This is firmly supported by the response of the economy to the expansionary fiscal policy of the last five years. Technological change, on the other hand, has been a major factor in the displacement and temporary unemployment of particular workers. Thus, technological change, along with other forms of economic change, is an important determinant of the precise places, industries, and people affected by unemployment. But the general level of demand for goods and services is by far the most important factor determining how many are affected, how long they stay unemployed, and how hard it is for new entrants to the labor market to find jobs.

The basic fact is that technology eliminates jobs, not work. It is the continuous obligation of economic policy to match increases in productive potential with increases in purchasing power and demand. Otherwise the potential created by technical progress runs to waste in idle capacity, unemployment, and deprivation.

General Levels of Unemployment

Changes in the volume of unemployment are governed by three fundamental forces: the growth of the labor force, the increase in output per man-hour, and the growth of the total demand for goods and services. Changes in the average hours of work enter in exactly parallel fashion, but have been quantitatively less significant. As productivity rises, less labor is required per dollar of national product, or more goods and services can be produced with the same number of man-hours. If output does not grow, employment will certainly fall; if production increases more rapidly than productivity (less any decline in average hours worked) employment must rise. But the labor force grows too. Unless Gross National Product (total final expenditure for goods and services, corrected for price changes) rises more rapidly than the sum of productivity increase and labor force growth (again modified for any change in hours of work), the increase in employment will be inadequate to absorb the growth in the labor force. Inevitably, the unemployment rate will increase. Only when total production expands faster than the rate of labor force growth *plus* the rate of productivity increase and *minus* the rate at which average hours fall does the unemployment rate fall. Figure 2 shows the year-to-year increases in GNP that were required during the 1950–64 period to maintain the previous year's volume of unemployment, and compares these with the actual GNP in these years. Figure 3 shows that increases in productivity were more important than growth of the labor force as sources of wide gains in output experienced since 1947. These increases in potential production simply were not matched by increases in demand adequate to maintain steady full employment.

In the late 1950s productivity and labor force were increasing more rapidly than usual, while the growth rate of output was lower than usual. This accounts for the persistence of high unemployment rates.

Throughout the postwar period output per man-hour in the private economy rose at an average trend rate of 3.2 per cent a year. (See Figure 4. For purely statistical reasons the figure is lowered to 2.8 per cent when government employees are included in any calculation of the rate of growth of output required to reduce unemployment.) The labor force had been growing at about 1 per cent a year from 1947 to 1953, a reflection of the low birth rates of the 1930s; between 1953 and 1960 it speeded up to 1.5 per cent. Average hours worked per year have been

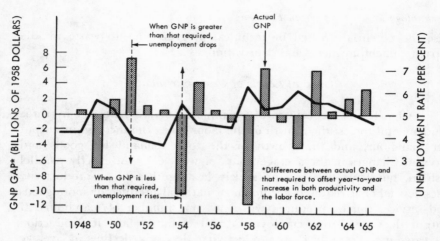

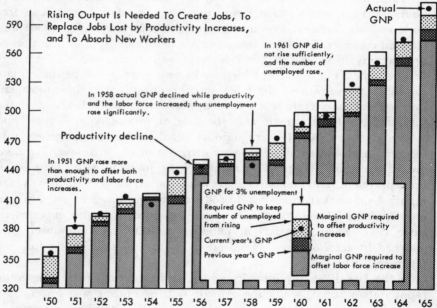

Figure 2. Gross National Product[1] Required to Offset Marginal Increases in Both Productivity[2] and the Labor Force (Compared with Actual GNP and with GNP for 3 Per Cent Unemployment[3])

[1]The gross national product figures shown are based on actual productivity statistics.

[2]Productivity refers here to output (measured by GNP) per employee (total U. S. employment) and does not take into account changes in hours worked.

[3]The use of 3 per cent unemployment is illustrative and in no way indicated that the Commission considers it an acceptable level of unemployment.

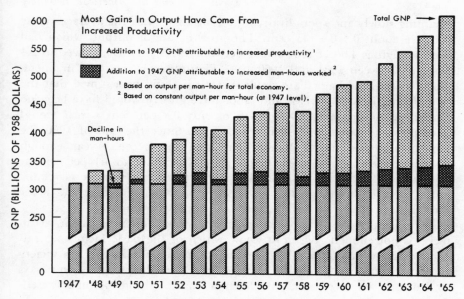

Figure 3. Source of Gross National Product Increases, 1947-65

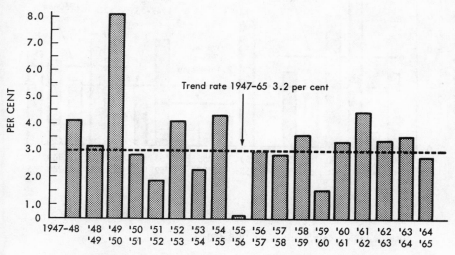

Figure 4. Annual Rate of Change of Output per Man-Hour,[1] 1947-65

[1]Based on total private economy.

declining slowly and sporadically for a long time, with the average yearly decrease about 0.3–0.4 per cent. The growth rate of output, which had been as high as 4.9 per cent a year between 1947 and 1953, slowed to 2.4 per cent between 1953 and 1960. (See Figure 5.) An increase in unemployment was the immediate result. Yet (if it could be assumed that the rate of productivity increase and labor force growth would have been no higher) an addition to GNP growth of only 0.4 per cent a year would have prevented unemployment from rising. Since the end of 1960 the growth rate has averaged slightly more than 4.5 per cent a year, enough to reduce the unemployment rate from 5.6 per cent to 4.1 per cent at the end of 1965. In only six of the past twelve years was the economic growth rate high enough to offset both productivity increase and labor force growth. In the other six years, unemployment rose.

But if part of the national purpose is to reduce unemployment, arithmetic is not enough. We must know which of the basic factors we can control and which we actually wish to control. For example, if a society chose to reduce the growth of productivity, it could probably find ways to frustrate its own creativity. Such a choice would be utterly self-defeating in its impact on living standards and wages.

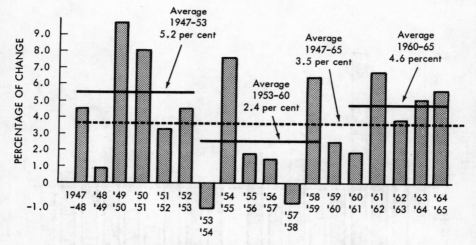

Figure 5. Annual Rate of Change in Gross National Product,[1] 1947-65

[1]Revised GNP data, in constant 1958 dollars.

Another way to limit unemployment would be to slow the growth of the labor force by encouraging later entry, earlier retirement, lower participation by some groups, or reduced hours of work. In the past, rising productivity has been realized partly in the form of higher incomes and partly in reduced working time and shorter working life. This pattern is likely to continue. We emphasize that the only truly useful way to reduce involuntary unemployment is to increase the growth of output.

The high unemployment that led to the formation of this Commission was the consequence of passive public policy, not the inevitable consequence of the pace of technological change. The experience of the economy during the life of this Commission is the best evidence that economic growth can continue to offset the growth of productivity and of the labor force and reduce unemployment further. We believe that continued reduction in unemployment is not only feasible but also a matter of urgency. The task will be a challenging one under the circumstances of the coming years.

In the decade ahead we do not expect output per man-hour in the whole economy to rise at a rate much faster than the 2.8 per cent a year characteristic of the postwar period. Some moderate acceleration may take place in the longer run. The growth of the labor force, however, is predictable and will be dramatic. It will increase about 1.9 per cent a year during the next five years, and almost as fast in the following ten or fifteen years. We expect a continued slow decline in hours of work. It follows that the output of the economy, and the aggregate demand to buy it, must grow in excess of 4 per cent a year just to prevent the unemployment rate from rising, and even faster if the unemployment rate is to fall further, as we believe it should. Yet our economy has seldom, if ever, grown at a rate faster than 3.5 per cent for any extended length of time. We have no cause for complacency. Positive fiscal, monetary, and manpower policies will be needed in the future as in the past. The nation should not be lulled into forgetfulness by a short-run need for increased defense expenditures.

Involvement of Technological Change in Particular Unemployment

To absolve technological change of major responsibility for high general levels of unemployment is not to deny its involvement in the displacement of particular individuals in particular occupations and industries. There are many causes of displacement. The demand for a product may decline, perhaps in a general cyclical downturn, perhaps because consumer tastes change. A new product or a newly invented process may capture a market from an existing producer. A company or an industry may change its location, perhaps in search of lower wage rates or raw materials sources, or because a technological change in transportation affects the relative advantages of being near raw materials sources or near markets. An employer may find himself in an unfavorable competitive position because of technological backwardness, his own inefficiency, or for reasons beyond his control. A major technological development may displace an entire occupational group within a plant. An accretion of small changes may increase productivity more rapidly than output rises and natural attrition can absorb.

Employment shifts, whether by industry or occupation or by establishment, are only an indication, not a measure, of the displacement of individuals. Employment changes within an establishment may not enter the statistics at all. Jobs may disappear, but the workers may be absorbed in other parts of the establishment. Employment in one firm may decline but be offset by increases in another, leaving industry totals unaffected. There are, however, offsetting forces. Some workers quit voluntarily, retire, or die. A fall in employment which does not exceed this attrition rate need not result in displacement. On the other hand, some of the voluntary quits may be in anticipation of layoffs and therefore represent a hidden displacement.

Nor is there a good measure of the distress caused by displacement. Everything depends on the difficulty with which a new job is obtained, its location, and its relative benefits. If the economic environment is favorable and the displaced worker has attractive skills, the distress need not be great. If the contrary, the human costs of displacement may be high. Under the best of circumstances a loss of accumulated job rights and a lower wage are likely consequences. The most serious adjustment problems have resulted when massive displacement has occurred among workers with overspecialized skills in isolated areas without alternative sources of employment. Coal miners are a prime example. The most profound of all displacements has been that in agriculture, where, in the postwar period, a 5.7 per cent annual rate of productivity increase accompanied by only a 1.4 per cent increase in farm output has reduced the number of farm owners and farm workers from 8.2 million in 1947 to 4.8 million in 1964, or 42.3 per cent. Those who left by the door marked "education" entered a new productive life. Too many, suffering from deficient rural educations, lacking skills in demand in urban areas, unaccustomed to urban ways, and often burdened by racial discrimination, exchanged rural poverty for an urban ghetto. How many of the 4.8 million workers who remain in agriculture are underemployed is conjectural, but the number is probably high.

Influence of Skill and Education on Unemployment

Unemployment has been concentrated among those with little education or skill, while employment has been rising most rapidly in those occupations generally considered to be the most skilled and to require the most education. This conjunction raises the question whether technological progress may induce a demand for very skilled and highly educated people in numbers our society cannot yet provide, while at the same time leaving stranded many of the unskilled and poorly educated with no future opportunities for employment.

As our society extends secondary and higher education to ever larger fractions of the population, it is necessary that the number of suitable and rewarding jobs increase correspondingly. Otherwise a different kind of frustration would result. We must, then, ask a much more subtle question: Is the demand for highly educated people outrunning the supply, and is the supply of unskilled workers outrunning the demand? It is difficult to establish any answer because occupational content can change while the occupational title remains the same, and because it is often unclear which occupations make greater demands in skill and education. Even if we were confident that there are imbalances between skills demanded and skills supplied, it would not follow that the source of the imbalance is technological. Japan and Western Europe operate sophisticated industrial economies with educational profiles far inferior to our own, and there is reason to believe that a highly automated economy could be engineered to fit a variety of educational profiles.

There is little doubt that the occupational structure of the American labor force is changing and will continue to change. Perhaps the main reason for this is the rapid growth of industries which employ predominantly white-collar and professional workers—education, finance, insurance, health, and business services. Another reason is the rapid improvement in educational attainment itself. Technological change within industries does not seem to be the major factor, except as regards the declining employment of laborers. Whether changes in the demand for different skills are to a substantial extent placing the new jobs beyond the reach of those losing other jobs can best be assessed by examining the relationship between educational attainment and educational requirements.

The evidence is at best fragmentary, but the Commission is impressed with labor market developments during the business expansion following the tax reduction of early 1964. As the general unemployment rate has fallen, the improvement has been greatest for those with the least education. In 1965 the unemployment rate for those with eight years of schooling or less fell from 7.6 to 5.9 per cent; for high school graduates with no further education, from 4.8 to 4.1 per cent; and for college graduates, only from 1.5 to 1.4 per cent.

It is the proper function of a market to allocate resources, and in this respect the labor market does not function differently from any other. If the available resources are of high quality, the market will adjust to the use of high quality resources; if the quality is low, methods will be developed to use such resources. In an efficient market, the choice between low-skill and high-skill manpower and between labor-intensive and capital-intensive production methods is made on the basis of relative costs. Although employment of unskilled, untrained labor can be encouraged by lowering its cost relative to that of skilled, trained labor, a better way would be to generate higher rates of economic activity. (In the same way, labor and machines "compete" with each other.) In a slack labor market employers must have some means of selecting among numerous applicants, and it is not surprising that educational attainment is often used as a convenient yardstick, regardless of its direct relevance to the requirements of the job.

We have found it useful to view the labor market as a gigantic "shape-up," with members of the labor force queued in order of their relative attractiveness to employers. If the labor market operates efficiently, employers will start at the head of the line, selecting as many as they need of employees most attractive to them. Their choice may be based on objective standards relating to ability, or on dubious standards of race, sex, or age; wage differentials may also be important; and formal education may be used as a rough screening device. The total number employed and unemployed depends primarily on the general state of economic activity. The employed tend to be those near the beginning and the unemployed those near the end of the line. Only as demand rises will employers reach further down the line in their search for employees.

If the relative disadvantages of the unskilled and uneducated have increased in recent years, the main reason is that the economy is less, not more, likely to run out of skilled and educated men and women. Thus the important factor is the impressive gain in the educational attainment of the labor force. (See Figure 6.) The proportion of workers aged eighteen years and over who have completed high school has risen from 43.3 to 57.5 per cent since 1952; those with four years or more of college, from 8 to 11.6 per cent.

Differential levels of educational attainment by age and color are

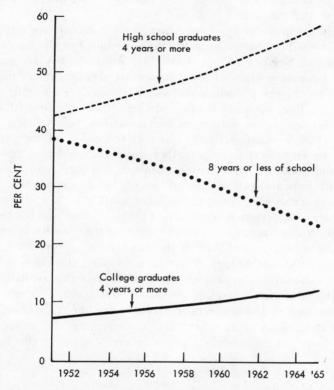

SOURCE: U. S. Bureau of the Census and U. S. Department of Labor.

Figure 6. Educational Attainment of the Civilian Labor Force,[1] Selected Years, 1952-65

[1]18 years old and over.

particularly noticeable. Every age group has shared in the upgrading, but in 1965, 70.2 per cent of workers age eighteen to thirty-four years had at least completed four years of high school, while only 46.3 per cent of those in the 45–64 age group had done so. Of the younger age group 11.7 per cent had completed four years or more of college, compared with 10.3 per cent of the older group. The disadvantage associated with color is shocking: of all nonwhites in the labor force eighteen years and older in 1965, 37.6 per cent had only elementary school education, 37.5

per cent had completed high school, and only 7 per cent had at least four years of college. The comparable figures for white workers were 21.6, 60, and 12.2 per cent.

It is inevitable in a society where educational standards are improving that the young will be better educated than the old. But the educational disadvantages of Negroes are not inevitable, although they are real and tragic. And because workers of low educational attainment are the least desirable to employers, nonwhite and older workers are concentrated at the rear of the line, not only because of their lower educational attainment but also because of deliberate discrimination. Nevertheless, whatever the level of economic activity, whatever the extent of the pressures of demand on employers to seek further down the ladder of education and skill, and whatever other hiring standards are used, education and training can improve the ability of people with competitive disadvantages to compete effectively in the labor market.

But a sharp distinction is necessary. The individual's education and skill are indeed important determinants of his relative ability to compete for jobs. The education and skill of the labor force is important to the economy's vitality. Technology determines, in part, the skills required and the educational component of those skills. But the availability of skills and the educational level of the labor force are also determinants of the technological changes which occur. Together, education, skill, and technology, along with other factors, determine the structure of employment and unemployment. They do not determine the level of either.

The Impact of Technological Change Upon Employment: The Next Ten Years

The level of employment depends primarily upon public policy, but assuming an unemployment rate of 3 per cent, 88.7 million people will be employed in 1975—18.3 million more than in 1964. In this eleven-year period the number employed will show an average increase of nearly 1.7 million a year, compared with an annual increase of 1.1 million between 1960 and 1965, and 1.8 million between 1964 and 1965.

Farm employment is expected to decline by about 1 million in spite of an increase of a third in farm output. To offset this displacement, all other employment is expected to increase by more than 19 million to achieve the net increase of 18.3 million jobs. The nonfarm goods-producing industries (manufacturing, mining, and construction) should show an employment gain of about 17 per cent, a rate somewhat faster than that achieved in the period 1947–64. The service-producing sector of the economy (trade, finance, services, and transportation and public utilities) is expected to grow by 38 per cent, also somewhat faster than in the last seventeen years.

Employment in the total goods-producing sector, including agriculture, will decline from about 41 per cent of all jobs in 1964 to 36 per cent in 1975. Employment in the broad service-producing sector will grow from about 59 per cent to 64 per cent of all jobs over the same period.

Despite fears that the impact of technological change will drastically reduce the demand for less-skilled workers, there will be about as many low-skill jobs in 1975 as there were in 1964, although their proportion will continue to decline as a percentage of all jobs.

The greatest increase in job opportunities will be for professional and technical workers: more than 4.5 million additional workers will be needed in these categories. The white-collar group as a whole is expected to expand by nearly two fifths and to constitute 48 per cent of all manpower requirements in 1975. The blue-collar occupations are expected to expand at less than half this rate and will make up about 34 per cent of all requirements. A 35 per cent increase in the demand for service workers is expected.

If nonwhites continue to hold the same proportion of jobs in each occupation as they held in 1964, the nonwhite unemployment rate in 1975 will be more than five times that for the labor force as a whole. In 1964 the nonwhite unemployment rate was 9.8 per cent, about twice that for whites. If upgrading of nonwhites continues as in the recent past, the nonwhite unemployment rate in 1975 would still be about two and a half times that for the labor force as a whole.

If all occupations have the same composition by age in 1975 as in 1964, opportunities for young people in the age bracket 14–24 will be substantially fewer than the number in this age group seeking work. Thus, the present high unemployment rate among young people threatens to worsen unless utilization patterns change. There is here a clear need for action.

It is difficult at best to separate the technological causes from the other causes that underlie the shifting employment patterns we have been discussing. To the displaced worker, or even to the maker of public policy, the precise cause of displacement may not even seem important. Because society gains from the flexibility and responsiveness that are the sources of displacement, it is society's responsibility to see that alternative opportunities are available and that blameless individuals do not bear excessive costs.

III.   CREATING AN ENVIRONMENT FOR ADJUSTMENT TO CHANGE: EMPLOYMENT AND INCOME

Constant displacement is the price of a dynamic economy. History suggests that it is a price worth paying. But the accompanying burdens and the benefits should be fairly distributed, and this has not always been the case. The costs of displacement to employees do not exhaust the total costs of technical and economic change. Business firms, labor unions, schools, government agencies, and other institutions, as well as individuals, develop some vested interest in the *status quo*. An economic or technological change that represents progress to society as a whole may be resisted by individuals and institutions to whom it appears a threat. Though public policy has less obligation to the perpetuation of institutions than to individuals, there is a public interest in reducing resistance to change.

The Management of Total Demand

It is the unanimously held conviction of the Commission that the most important condition for successful adjustment to technological change is an adequate level of total income and employment. We recognize that this is not the end of economic policy, but we are confident it is the beginning.

During the life of the Commission the very groups disproportionately burdened by unemployment—the young and inexperienced, the under-educated, the unskilled, Negroes, production workers—have profited more than proportionately from the healthy growth of total employment.

We believe that the potential for general expansion of demand and employment has not yet been exhausted. It is not our business to predict what will occur during the next twelve months, either in Asia or in the domestic economy. We urge, however, that the toleration of unnecessary unemployment is a very costly way to police inflation. It deprives the country of valuable output, and it sacrifices the poorest and least privileged of our citizens. For the longer run, we believe it to be of the highest importance to the future of democracy in the world that this country never present to its neighbors the spectacle of wartime prosperity yielding to peacetime unemployment.

Some combination of tax reduction (leading to higher private spending) and increased public expenditure will be required to stimulate the economy when stimulus is needed. The choice between them depends on our national priorities; a balanced policy will in the long run surely include both. It is clear, however, that the nation faces a large backlog of unmet human and community needs as a consequence of depression, war, and high defense spending. The needs in education, health, transportation, pollution control, and similar areas are obvious to almost everyone. It is our considered judgment that in selection of economic stimulants, major attention should be given to public investment expenditures, some of which we shall mention later in this report.

Public Service Employment

How much unemployment should our society tolerate? We are not impressed with a 4 per cent unemployment rate, or a 3 per cent rate, or any other rate as an ultimate goal of economic policy. This Commission takes seriously the commitment of the Employment Act of 1946 to provide "useful employment opportunities for all those able, willing, and seeking to work." This cannot mean literally zero unemployment since in a free economy there will always be some turnover, voluntary and involuntary. It does mean limiting unemployment to the minimum necessary for the smooth functioning of a free labor market.

The Neighborhood Youth Corps and several other provisions of the Economic Opportunity Act recognize the anomaly of excessive unemployment in a society confronted with a huge backlog of public service needs in its parks, its streets, its slums, its countryside, its schools, its libraries, its hospitals, its rest homes, its public buildings—throughout the public and nonprofit sectors of the economy. These new programs, like the public works programs of the 1930s, recognize that employing the unemployed is almost costless. The unemployed consume; they do not produce. To provide them with meaningful jobs increases not only their income but also that of society. Much of the work that needs doing calls for limited skills and minor amounts of training. Some of it is manual, some of it is subprofessional.

The principle of public service employment has been implicitly endorsed in existing programs. We recommend that the concept be made explicit and expanded as a permanent program. Since such a program would provide services for which society has growing need, no element of make-work would be involved.

The major resources must come from the federal government. The jobs need not. Table 3 lists some areas of the economy where important social needs are now inadequately met. A federal funding agency could provide program approval and financial administration. State and local governments and certain kinds of nonprofit institutions, as well as federal agencies, could provide the jobs. The objective should be to use available labor productively without drawing workers from existing jobs or subverting prevailing labor standards. The wages should in no case be lower than the federal minimum wage, with the possible exception of a partial exemption for youth.

We therefore recommend (a) that public service employment be provided for those unsuccessful in the competition for existing jobs; (b) that a five-year program be established, the amount of public service employment to be increased each year, depending upon previous experience and labor market conditions; (c) that an initial sum of perhaps $2 billion be appropriated to provide about 500,000 additional full-time public service jobs; and (d) that the program be coupled with a serious effort to learn more about the causes of "hard-core" unemployment.

Income Maintenance

Even this program will not meet the problem of giving all our citizens a decent standard of living. There are some whose productivity

Table 1. Estimates of Potential Sources of New Jobs Through Public Service Employment[1]

Source of employment	Job potential (in millions)
Medical institutions and health services	1.2
Educational institutions	1.1
National beautification	1.3
Welfare and home care	0.7
Public protection	0.35
Urban renewal and sanitation	0.65
Total	5.3

[1]Estimated from various unpublished sources.

is reduced by physical and mental incapacity, some are too old to work, and there are tens of thousands of families without breadwinners. Such individuals and families are not necessarily the victims of technological progress. Nevertheless, income maintenance for them must also be considered in this report, not only for completeness, but also because we owe to the advance of technology much of the productive capacity that permits us, as a nation, to tackle the problem. Our concern here is for economic progress, not fear of technological change.

WAGE-RELATED SOCIAL INSURANCE PROGRAMS

Most people who spend the greater part of their adult life working can protect themselves against loss of income due to death, disability, old age, or unemployment through social insurance programs. In these programs benefits are related to wages and paid as a matter of right; they do not require a means or income test.

Improvement in our unemployment insurance system could directly facilitate adjustment to change. Particular attention must be given to the needs of those with long records of steady employment who suddenly find themselves permanent victims of economic or technological change.

Average Old Age and Survivors and Disability Insurance benefits are currently less than $1000 a year. We find this inadequate; we recommend that benefit standards be lifted. Benefits under Workmen's Compensation are also in need of reform.

PUBLIC ASSISTANCE

Public assistance programs, as part of an income maintenance system, provide minimum income support, usually but not exclusively for families without a breadwinner, on the basis of proved need. Recipients of public assistance do not receive benefits as a matter of right, as in the case of social insurance. In principle, welfare payments are limited by a strict means test to the difference between some minimum standard and a family's resources from earnings. This has the absurd consequence that additional earnings are taxed 100 per cent. Unless the family can earn enough to dispense with public assistance entirely, it loses a dollar of welfare payments for every dollar it is able to earn. It would be hard to imagine a system better calculated to discourage self-help.

In many communities, welfare payments cannot be made to families with an able-bodied adult male in residence. Consequently, fathers are encouraged to desert their destitute families to make them eligible for public assistance.

Perhaps the system's most serious faults are the stringency of need tests and the small size of payments. The average payment per recipient under the program of aid to families with dependent children is $34 a month. Fewer than one quarter of the 35 million people now living in poverty in the U.S. receive any type of public assistance, and fewer than one third of the 15 million children living in poverty benefit from public assistance. The Commission feels strongly that a better integrated and more comprehensive system of social insurance and income maintenance is both necessary and feasible at this stage in our history.

The Commission recommends that Congress go beyond a reform of the present structure and examine wholly new approaches to the problem of income maintenance. In particular, we suggest that Congress give serious thought to a "minimum income allowance," or "negative income tax," program. Such a program, if found feasible, should be designed to approach by stages the goal of eliminating the need for a means test by providing a floor of adequate minimum incomes. A minimum income allowance would complete the symmetry of our tax system, under which tax payments are related to income, family size, and medical and other expenses, by acknowledging the continuity beyond zero tax rates. It seems anomalous to us that a family of five now pays the same tax (zero) whether its total income is $500 or $3500.

Income maintenance payments under any such scheme should be designed to eliminate the gap between reported income and an explicit minimum. The incentive to work can be preserved by a schedule reducing the allowance partially for an increase in earned income. By relieving the states of part of the burden of public assistance, the minimum income allowance would stabilize or even reduce a source of rapidly rising demand on their limited fiscal resources. If adopted, it would seem appropriate to introduce an income maintenance program in stages, as it becomes necessary to counter the fiscal drag in the present tax transfer structure. This is one of the few ways in which those with the very lowest incomes can share directly in tax reduction.

IV.   FACILITATING ADJUSTMENT TO CHANGE: PUBLIC POLICIES

We turn now to programs and policies that could facilitate adjustment to technological change in our economy and speed up the process of finding new jobs for those who are displaced for whatever reason. In this section of our report we shall describe how adjustment might be facilitated by education and training, by improving the flow of information in the labor market, by regional action, and by various techniques available to private employers.

Education and Training

Second in importance only to the provision of jobs in facilitating adjustment to technological and other change is the encouragement of an adaptable work force through education and training. We wish to emphasize at the outset, however, that we regard the goals of education as far transcending economic objectives. But from the purely economic point of view, education has three principal effects: (1) it can increase the versatility and adaptability of people and thus help them to adjust to change; (2) it can open up new opportunities of employment; and (3) it can increase the productivity of workers.

We strongly recommend, therefore, that educational opportunity be open to all. A first principle of a progressive and humane society is that no person shall be deprived by financial barriers—or by barriers of ethnic or national origin, religion, age, place of residence, or family background —of the opportunity for maximum growth and development through education. We offer these recommendations:

1. Perhaps the most serious deficiency in our educational system has been the inadequate opportunities available to those in greatest need, namely, children of families and communities where there is cultural deprivation, segregation, or isolation. At least 100,000 additional classrooms and 133,000 teachers would be necessary by 1970 to provide compensatory full-year education from ages three to five for all who are in need of it.

2. The quantity and quality of primary and secondary education, especially in low-income urban areas and rural backwaters, should be improved.

3. High school graduation should become universal. It is generally accepted that those with less than a sound high school education are unprepared for both employment and life. To accomplish this, both the problems of motivation and inadequate family income must both be faced realistically.

4. For most secondary school pupils vocational training should be deferred until after high school. General education is especially necessary in a rapidly changing economy in which versatility and flexibility are at a premium. The training for many—perhaps most—specific jobs can

and must be done on the job as a responsibility of the employer. However, properly designed vocational education can help implant the important understanding that education is a continuing process of self-renewal indispensable for continuing adaptability in a changing world.

5. A nationwide system of free public education through two years beyond high school (grade fourteen) should be established.

6. All qualified students should have realistic access to university education. No qualified student should be deprived of education at any level because of his family's lack of financial resources.

7. Education, training, and retraining should be available to individuals throughout their lives. The ability to manage change, whether to keep up with new developments in a profession or to retool for a new job, requires that further education be available when needed. Public education should provide a comprehensive program of educational opportunity for persons of all ages and of varying educational attainments. A system of education that is open-minded, with freedom for mature students to enter, leave when alternative experiences seem more fruitful, and then reenter, can be a reality through the coordinated efforts of public schools, community colleges, vocational schools, universities, and employers.

8. Of special importance is the need to provide more extensive educational opportunities for adults whose basic education is deficient. It must be recognized that every effort to improve the education of children now in school will increase the disadvantages of adults with substandard education. Recent developments in educational technology appear to have special applicability to the needs of the adult learner.

9. Workers should be given incentives to undertake full-time educational programs during periods of layoff and during negotiated sabbatical leaves.

10. The task of expanding educational opportunity must also focus on those who appear unable to respond effectively to existing systems and methods. New educational technologies are under development that show promise of helping those who have been regarded as slow learners or as poorly motivated.

11. In retrospect, one of the highest return investments we as a nation have made was the GI bill following the Second World War and the Korean War. Not only did we aid veterans to make up lost years, but we brought about a veritable social revolution. Men and women whose backgrounds precluded the possibility of higher education and advanced training were lifted into totally unexpected positions in life. And in simple monetary terms, the investment has already been returned in

taxes on their higher incomes. The lesson should not be forgotten or neglected.

Matching Men and Jobs

Adjustment on the part of workers to technological and other change would be helped by improved operation of the labor market. Frictional unemployment can be minimized only if workers seeking jobs and employers seeking workers can be efficiently brought together.

LABOR MARKET INFORMATION

The United States Employment Service and its affiliated state agencies supply increasing amounts of information about local employment trends. But there is simply no place in any local labor market—let alone a regional or national one—where an individual job seeker (or employer) can discover the full range of jobs (or employees) available to him. We have two suggestions to offer:

1. To give job seekers specific information about job openings and employers specific information about potential employees, the Commission recommends the creation of a computerized nationwide service for matching men and jobs. It would seem particularly fitting that the computer, the very device that has been blamed for much displacement, could be turned into a vital tool for facilitating adjustment to change.

The proposed computerized communication system could be organized in several ways. It could be a nonprofit public service corporation with joint public and private ownership, or it could be part of the United States Employment Service. Some Commission members believe that the first-mentioned form of organization would encourage widespread use of the service.

2. To warn of vulnerability to displacement and to aid rational choice among alternatives, forecasts of occupational demand and manpower availability, locally and regionally, should be improved and made more readily available.

THE PUBLIC EMPLOYMENT SERVICE

The public employment service is federally financed but state operated. There is a wide disparity in the effectiveness of the services from state to state. Many factors are at work to make the present system much less effective than it should be. We believe, therefore, that the public employment service should be made a federal agency and then be provided with the resources to do its job.[2]

GEOGRAPHIC RELOCATION

While it is essential to encourage labor mobility, emphasis should be placed on attempts to rehabilitate economically distressed areas through regional planning and through federal financial and technical assistance. We should try to bring jobs to areas where workers live and to make full use of existing investments in community facilities, such as schools and churches. We commend the continuing experimentation that is going into the rehabilitation of Appalachia and other depressed areas.

Another important obstacle to the geographical relocation of men and jobs remains almost unnoticed. Part of the postwar displacement has resulted from the desire of industry to follow white-collar workers to the suburbs, while the poor remain trapped in the central city. If one is too poor to own an automobile, it may be literally true that "you can't get there from here." A solution to this problem is essential, not only for adjustment to technological change but also to attack poverty and reduce the grievances that lead to riots and strife.

ELIMINATING SOCIAL BARRIERS TO EMPLOYMENT

The process of successful adjustment to change can also be impeded by any number of social barriers that bar certain workers from certain jobs. These practices include discrimination based on race, age, and sex, together with arbitrary control over hiring or training in certain apprenticeship programs.

This Commission has taken special cognizance of the civil rights "revolution." The heart of the problem faced by Negroes, as they strive to enter the mainstream of American economic life, is employment opportunity. A healthy, rapidly growing economy is a necessary condition of Negro progress. But by itself it is probably not enough.

For more than three hundred years the Negro has been systematically denied his rightful place in American society. This denial has taken its toll in many ways. In order to develop and use fully the potential of America's Negroes, special programs will be needed—programs that attempt in one or two decades to compensate for three hundred years of systematic deprivation. The cost of these programs will be high, but it

[2]Philip Sporn and Patrick E. Haggerty disassociated themselves from this recommendation.

will be small in relation to the human costs of generations of suffering, and it will also be small in relation to the benefits society will reap.

Facilitating Regional Adjustment[3]

All regions have not shared equally in the unprecedented economic growth that this nation has enjoyed since the end of the Second World War. The economies of many regions have, in fact, declined, leaving pools of unemployment, poverty, and hardship. In a dynamic economy characterized by technological change as well as by shifts in demand, depletion of resources, and other factors, such geographic inequities can perhaps be expected, but this does not lessen the hardships involved.

There are no easy solutions to the problems posed by regional economic dislocation. In the final analysis, however, the nation is faced with the choice of rebuilding and assisting distressed communities until they become self-sustaining, or of abandoning them altogether. This Commission believes that a concerted effort to revitalize potentially viable communities is required. Such assistance should be designed to encourage community self-help and with the needs of the entire regional economy in mind. The types of assistance needed include the following:

1. A comprehensive economic analysis must be the first step.

2. Whenever possible, new technological developments should be used to stimulate regional economic growth.

3. Venture capital is required to permit each region to take full advantage of the opportunities presented by technological change.

4. Direct financial assistance is needed to help distressed communities update and improve local water, sewerage, highway, and other facilities. Improved schools and other institutions for upgrading human resources are particularly important.

The Federal Reserve System seems to offer the most viable mechanism for developing and implementing regional programs.[4] Federal Reserve Districts have several advantages as bases for regional development programs: they approximate existing regional economies, and they are already established. And, since the Federal Reserve System is closely associated with private banking institutions, it could effectively stimulate the application of private funds to the development of local and regional economies. Specific recommendations in this respect include the following:

[3]Philip Sporn disassociated himself from this section.
[4]Joseph A. Beirne, Albert J. Hayes and Walter P. Reuther disassociated themselves from the recommendations involving the Federal Reserve System.

1. Each Federal Reserve Bank should establish a regular program of regional economic analysis to permit constant evaluation of the problems and opportunities facing the region.

2. Each Federal Reserve District should establish an advisory council for economic growth composed of leaders from business, labor, government, universities, and other interested groups.

3. Capital banks should be established within each Federal Reserve District to provide venture capital and long-term financing for new and existing companies.

4. Regional technical institutes should be established within each region to keep abreast of new technological developments.

5. A high-level federal executive is needed within each region to coordinate the efforts of various existing federal programs at the regional level.

The nation can meet its goal of maximum economic growth and its commitment to provide all its citizens with the opportunity to share in the national prosperity only when the resources available in all sections of the country are fully used. The recommendations outlined are designed to meet this goal.

V.   FACILITATING ADJUSTMENT TO CHANGE: PRIVATE POLICIES

The emphasis placed thus far on public policy is not intended to imply that the federal government has the sole responsibility for accomplishing adjustment to technological change. Such adjustment occurs constantly without governmental assistance. Indeed, one of the principal strengths of our private enterprise system is its flexibility in permitting changes to occur.

Requirements for Adjustment

An adequate private adjustment program would satisfy certain basic requirements.

1. Workers displaced by change would be offered a substantially equivalent or better job, or the training required to fill such a job.

2. They would be guaranteed adequate financial security while searching for alternative jobs or while undertaking training.

3. They would be given financial aid to relocate their families whenever this becomes necessary.

4. They would not lose earned security rights, such as vacation, retirement, insurance, and related credits.

Many private adjustment programs go far toward meeting these basic requirements, but their extent is uncertain. The Labor and Commerce Departments should undertake systematic investigation and reporting about them to permit more extensive communication about effective adjustment programs among and between employers, employees, and unions.

Methods of Facilitating Adjustment to Change

There is general agreement that, wherever possible, reductions in the work force necessitated by technological change should be accomplished by attrition, that is, by the simple expedient of not replacing workers who leave, retire, or die. By studying attrition ratios and the age structure of the work force, and by attempting to project manpower requirements, employers could do a better job of integrating hiring and layoff policies under conditions of technological change.

Because laid-off employees need time to explore alternative job opportunities, government agencies, unions, and others have increasingly emphasized the need for an "early warning system" to alert employees to the possibility or inevitability of future compulsory job changes. Recent research suggests that employer fears of premature job-changing are largely unfounded, especially if employees must forgo severance pay and related assistance should they depart before jobs have been terminated. Employees should be given time off with pay to look for other jobs or financial assistance while they upgrade their skills through additional training or education.

It is now generally conceded that the most efficient method of training workers for existing job vacancies is by instruction on the job. However, sufficient knowledge about the potential capacities of employees is lacking; consequently, many are not being trained for jobs they could perform. The most frequently cited example of this deficiency is management's failure to promote more blue-collar workers to white-collar jobs, even though many skilled craftsmen are quite capable of learning work now assigned to junior engineers and white-collar technicians.

Protecting the Earned Benefit Rights of Displaced Employees

The principal device developed by American unions to protect the job interests of those they represent is seniority, a system of employment preference based on length of service. Employees with the longest service are given the greatest job security and the best opportunities for advancement. Seniority affects employees' economic security more than any other provision of the collective agreement.

The seniority principle has become so important that it is embodied in virtually every union contract, and it undoubtedly has exercised considerable influence on personnel policies of many nonunion firms. Seniority, however, does not create jobs, and therefore cannot be relied upon as the sole protection against technological change.

The loss of a job usually entails also loss of vacation eligibility, of various forms of insurance protection for the worker and his family, and, frequently, of pension rights as well. The loss of pension rights is particularly serious since the worker cannot relive the years during which he accumulated the pension entitlement that vanished with his job.

Many assert that pension benefits should be "portable," in order not to inhibit labor mobility, and that in any event pensions are a form of deferred wages which belong to employees. Whatever the merit of opposing arguments, the most recent survey by the United States Bureau of Labor Statistics shows that more than two thirds of private pension plans, covering 60 per cent of employees with private pension rights, included some form of vesting. The Commission takes no position on the adequacy of the pace of this development but hopes that the movement toward portability and vesting will continue.

An increasing number of workers participate in group plans for life and health insurance at substantially reduced rates. Severance of employment may present the employee with the equally impractical choices of forfeiting these benefits or converting them to individual policies at prohibitive cost. Increased efforts should be devoted to making such benefits portable also. Careful study should be given to a legislative system for reinsurance for private pension plans and other earned benefits similar to the reinsurance of bank deposits through the Federal Deposit Insurance Corporation.

Hours of Work, Leisure, and the Adjustment Process

Full employment is not the only requirement for free choice between work and leisure. Under present practices, the tendency is to force choice between an arbitrary pattern of work and no job at all. Industry needs to develop a more flexible system of determining work schedules. The increasing numbers of youth and women in the labor force indicate the rising demand for part-time jobs. Insofar as any industry can develop its program of production to accommodate itself to employ even a small percentage of its work force on a part-time basis, it needs to implement the concept. We should, and no doubt will, continue to use a portion of rising productivity to add to leisure. Such increased leisure can take a number of forms; periodic extended vacation periods; more holidays; earlier retirement, including "phased retirement" permitting gradual reduction in the length of the workday or week commencing a few years before actual retirement; sabbatical leaves to provide opportunities for extended physical rest, personal reappraisal, retraining, and additional education; and, of course, reduced hours of work. Serious attempts should also be made to come to grips with the problem of introducing flexibility into weekly work schedules.

Collective Bargaining and the Management of Change

Collective bargaining has proved to be an excellent vehicle for the effective management of change. It permits those directly affected by the change to deal with it firsthand and with a familiarity that takes into account the special problems peculiar to an enterprise. But despite its many successes, collective bargaining has sometimes failed spectacularly to deal with the problems presented by change. We have two suggestions to offer:

1. Unions and employers could call on government for greater assistance without jeopardizing the private nature of the bargaining process. Greater use of government research would contribute considerably to the soundness of private judgments.

2. Basic issues such as adjustment to technological change cannot be solved by a small team of negotiators working under the pressure of a deadline. Such issues must be dealt with patiently, carefully, and, above all, continuously until satisfactory solutions emerge. This kind of bargaining calls for ability of the highest order on the part of both labor and management. If technological change can be viewed as an opportunity to be embraced rather than as a cataclysm to be avoided at all costs, then the workers' defense mechanism described by Veblen as "the conscientious withdrawal of efficiency" will gradually give way to a spirit of accommodation and cooperation.

Other Private and Public Efforts To Manage Change and Facilitate Adjustment

Although development of private adjustment programs is principally the responsibility of the parties immediately involved, they can obtain useful assistance from outside private organizations as well as from government.

Increased management concern for adequate solutions to adjustment problems is reflected in the STEP (Solutions to Employment Problems) program of the National Association of Manufacturers. Member companies are surveyed to ascertain the types of programs being used to deal with manpower problems; each program is verified by members of the STEP staff and evaluated in terms of its potential usefulness to firms seeking solutions to similar problems; then the case studies are summarized and circulated among member firms.

Another example of a well conceived approach to the solution of manpower problems is the National Skills Bank of the National Urban League, a computerized file of the capabilities of Negro job seekers. Although this program is directed mainly at trained persons whose skills are underused, the Urban League has also used it to screen people who need training and other remedial help and to refer them to available programs.

These new programs emphasize the need for longer-range and more systematic planning to prevent adjustment situations from becoming adjustment problems. And because most adjustment situations are relatively small, there is every reason to expect that such an approach can prove effective. Large displacements sometimes occur, however, and demand extraordinary efforts to deal with them. The closing of a large plant or the sudden cancellation of a major government contract can throw thousands of workers out of jobs overnight. When disastrous situations of this type occur, the federal government should coordinate and expedite both public and private job and retraining alternatives for the unemployed.

The Adjustment to Change by Minority Groups

The adjustment to technological as well as to economic and social change presents special problems for Negroes and other minority groups. Not until unions, employers, and private and public institutions are able to overcome the insidious vestiges of discrimination based on race, color, sex, religion, or national origin can the adjustment process be considered adequate for such groups.

At present the economic opportunities of Negroes are barred by exclusive hiring practices, discriminatory promotion policies, and unreasonable and unnecessarily restrictive hiring requirements. Every form of discrimination based on race, color, sex, or religion must be overcome.

Many individual employers and unions as well as the AFL-CIO were speaking out against racial and ethnic discrimination in employment before the Civil Rights Act of 1964 was passed, and they played major roles in bringing about the enactment of that statute and other civil rights legislation. However, even in those international unions whose dedicated opposition to discrimination in employment is unchallenged, adherence to these principles is not always as steadfast at local levels, where regional and cultural influences sometimes outweigh organizational commitments. National multiplant corporations encounter similar problems with some of their local plant managers. It must be noted that some unions and some employers, and even some federal, state and local agencies, have a record of discrimination against Negroes and other minority groups that is a mockery of the basic principles of industrial democracy.

Literal adherence to the letter of the law, however, is simply not enough. Negroes and ethnic minorities need and are entitled to an affirmative assurance. Employers, including government agencies, should go into the Negro, Mexican-American, and Puerto Rican communities and actively recruit employees from among them. They should also lower minimum standards of employment for certain jobs with unnecessarily and unreasonably high requirements.

In addition to initiating these changes through collective bargaining, unions and managements that do not already do so must take steps to assure that national policies against discrimination are effectively implemented at the local level. Experience demonstrates that active cooperation of managements with unions greatly facilitates the elimination of discriminatory practices at the plant level. Although some progress has been made in opening skilled trades apprenticeship programs to members of minority groups, much more remains to be done. Discrimination is a national evil that must be eliminated on a national basis.

We believe that employers and unions alike have an affirmative duty to make special efforts to aid Negroes and members of other minority groups in obtaining more and better jobs. Such efforts will not in themselves redress the injustices that these disadvantaged citizens have already suffered, but surely they are the very least we should expect from those who profess a belief in democracy.

What has been said about racial and ethnic minorities applies, though to a lesser extent, to women and to older workers. Although discrimination against them is more easily masked and often justified by plausible reasons, no one can deny that there is widespread prejudice against employment of women and older workers as such. Such prejudice has no place in a society dedicated to providing every person willing and able to work with a useful and suitable job.

The Government as a Model Employer

Change and adjustment are not confined to the private sector alone. The federal government, with 2.5 million civilian employees, has a particular obligation to be a model employer in the management of change. We also believe the federal government could be a more positive influence by encouraging its contractors to make adequate provisions for displaced workers.

Federal protection of the earned work-life credits of its employees is, for the most part, excellent. But other federal practices leave much to be desired. For example, the federal government does not list all job vacancies with public employment services. Indeed, there is no central file of available jobs for the federal establishment, Federal agencies should make a determined effort to ensure that training and education resources are not disproportionately allocated to those with higher grades and skills. Moreover, education and training budgets of government agencies are frequently among the first to feel the effects of economy drives. Congress should help the agencies sustain their budget requests for training programs.

State and local governments should also conduct themselves as model employers in regard to adjustment to change.

The Government as an Experimenter in New Adjustment Techniques

The federal government is in an excellent position to experiment with new methods to increase work-life flexibility and adjustment techniques. For example, the federal government should take the initiative in expanding employment opportunities by removing what may be rather arbitrary entrance requirements for low-skill jobs. The problems and needs of older workers provide another opportunity for the government to seek creative new solutions. In short, the government should be in the forefront of experimentation in hiring, training, and facilitating adjustment to change.

VI. TECHNOLOGY AND UNMET HUMAN AND COMMUNITY NEEDS: GENERAL CONSIDERATIONS

Technology offers society an opportunity to realize an age-old vision: to enlarge the capacities of man and to extend his control over the environment. In directing the attention of this Commission to the impact of technology on society, the Congress wisely did not limit its instructions to the immediate tasks of assessing the effect of technology on employment and of recommending measures for easing adjustment to change. Congress also asked us to explore the future. The Commission was instructed to define "those areas of unmet community and human needs toward which the application of new technologies might most effectively be directed," to assess "the most effective means for channeling new technologies into promising directions," and to recommend steps "to promote technological changes in the continued economic growth and improved well-being of our people."

In effect, we were asked, What can our society have? How does society decide what it wants? How can it get what it wants? We approach these problems, fully aware of their complexity.

The Possibilities Available

As we have noted earlier in this report, output per man-hour has been increasing recently by about 3 per cent a year, a rate that doubles the national output in about twenty-four years. This establishes what our society can have. The fruits of this increase are available in various ways. If all the productivity increases of the next twenty years were taken in the form of added income, average per capita earnings would climb from a present annual figure of $3181 to $5802, an increase of 82 per cent. In the unlikely event that productivity gains were taken entirely in the expansion of leisure, the workweek could fall to twenty-two hours by 1985, or the work year could be cut to twenty-seven weeks, or the retirement age could be lowered to thirty-eight.

But productivity gains could be applied directly in still another way. We could use the gains to improve the nature and conditions of the work environment itself—to reduce monotony, enlarge the range of skills used in a job, encourage variety and rotation of assignments. In short, we could strive to make work a more satisfying experience.

Society, by communal choice, could also elect to use future gains in productivity to satisfy a broad range of unmet community needs. Thus, we have the option of using new technological means to improve the quality of American life.

A third broad option is to use a portion of our continuing gains to help the less fortunate in other parts of the world. Their problems are enormous. The question of how much aid can be given, and how much can be used, lies outside the charge of this Commission. As in the past, some share of our national income and our technologies will be committed to developing countries in the form of loans and direct aid.

The Matrix of Decisions

One of the difficulties is that economic goods are of two types: individual goods and social goods. Individual goods are divisible; each person can buy what he wants according to his wishes. Social goods are not divisible but are part of a communal service: national defense, public education, flood control, preservation of open space, and so on.

Individuals have their own scale of values which allows them to weigh relative satisfaction against costs and to make their purchases accordingly. Public life lacks such measures. We have no effective social calculus that gives us true valuation of all the costs and benefits of individual and social purchases.

The Commission has no pat solution for improving the decision-making process, but it has three suggestions it believes worthy of consideration:

1. The extension of technical research on our unmet human and community needs would itself demonstrate to the people and their leaders the possibilities of solutions, and thus lead to action.

2. We should try to improve our ability to recognize and evaluate social costs and benefits so that the public and its leaders are in a better position to weigh alternatives.

3. The public decision-making process might be improved by the creation of an appropriate body of high prestige and distinction, which would make a continuing study of national goals and evaluate the nation's progress toward the attainment of those goals.

VII.   APPLYING TECHNOLOGY TO COMMUNITY NEEDS

Our unmet human and community needs are vast, even in the wealthiest society the world has ever known. The Commission has selected health and the urban environment as examples both of the areas where application of technologies is needed and of the problems which impede their application.

In a predominantly private enterprise society, unmet needs tend to be of two kinds: (1) the private needs of low income people who are unable to buy housing and necessary services, and (2) those public needs of the whole nation which are not readily available in private markets. Some kind of minimum income maintenance has been discussed elsewhere in this report as an answer to the first. We limit ourselves here to the second category.

Why have not these needs been met? Our conviction, growing out of the spectacular achievements in military technology and our success in the conquest of space, is that the obstacles are not primarily technological. This does not imply that specific technologies are available in each area, although in many cases they are. Just as the concentration of research efforts produced such radically new innovations as intercontinental ballistic missiles and Polaris submarines, concentrations of similar scale on more difficult economic and social problems could contribute to meeting our human and community needs if the political consensus could be implemented.

Health Needs

The application of computers and electronic information processing to problems of health seems to offer great promise in the decade ahead. For example, automated "multiphasic" screening techniques have been developed through which hundreds of people could pass each hour, greatly raising the productivity of physicians. The establishment of health computer systems on a regional basis could provide regional data processing for automated clinical laboratories, automation of certain aspects of medical diagnosis, storage and rapid recall of individual health records, and collection and evaluation of important medical statistics.

Such systems could help provide better care for everyone, regardless of geographic location, reduce unit costs, and alleviate the manpower problem that regional medical programs and Medicare will intensify. The introduction of such new technological aids makes it important that we improve our health statistics.

Finally, the nation has a clear need for more physicians, nurses, and medical technicians in all categories. Government support will be required to create new medical schools, expand the enrollments of existing schools, and develop new methods of instruction.

The Urban Environment

By 1975 over three fourths of all Americans will be living in urban areas, including the suburbs. Total private and public spending for urban facilities of all kinds in 1962 was estimated at $64 billion. This includes housing, offices, schools, shopping centers, and highways. Unfortunately, the net result of much of this spending was to make cities less habitable by increasing the already congested traffic, the polluted air, and the number of drab housing projects.

TRANSPORTATION

The failure of our metropolitan regions to improve their steadily deteriorating public transportation services is now a familiar story. The problem remains unsolved largely because of the failure to look at transport technology as a whole. The various forms of transportation are subjected to various degrees of governmental regulation and to different subsidies.

A variety of promising new transport innovations and systems are beginning to emerge. The specific technologies need not concern us here. We recognize that, in the end, cost will be the decisive factor. But to gain a true picture of costs, including social costs, it is important that none of the new technologies be considered in isolation. Most of the new concepts involve a development effort greater than can be supported by private industry or by a single geographic region. They require federal support, and they must be part of an effort that views transportation as an interlocking problem—one that cannot be solved piecemeal, or with a single technology.

AIR AND WATER POLLUTION

Pollutants that contaminate our air and water supplies have increased alarmingly. Unfortunately, we still lack firm knowledge of the effects of many pollutants on plant life, animals, and human beings. Moreover, not all the technical means for reducing these hazards are available. But even with present technology enormously more could be done than has been done.

By far the most important barrier today to effective control of air and water pollution is economic. At all lower levels of government, pollution abatement must compete for funds with a host of other community needs. Private companies are understandably reluctant to invest large sums in pollution control equipment from which, in most cases, they can gain no competitive advantage. It is clear that some way must be found to assign costs of pollution abatement to the sources of pollutants, whether they be industrial, municipal, or individual.

In the last few years there has been a heartening upsurge of national concern about air and water pollution, and Congress has passed important measures directed toward the abatement of both hazards. Cities and states, too, have demonstrated a mood for stronger action. The Commission encourages the expansion of these efforts and urges an enlargement of research into the effects of pollutants so that wise pollution control policies and regulations can be developed.

HOUSING

The housing industry has been frequently criticized for its technological backwardness. The issue is incredibly complex, for the "blame," such as it is, rests on many: the fragmented industry, its unions, its suppliers, the mortgage bankers, local building codes, and finally consumers, who seem to prefer styles of housing that do not lend themselves to the most advanced techniques. For those who can afford the housing they prefer, there is little reason for public concern. It is upon those with low incomes that the high cost of housing imposes its burdens.

According to the 1960 Census of Housing, about 6.3 million households with incomes under $4000 and an additional 2.2 million households with incomes over $4000 lived in units that needed complete replacement. Approximately 1.5 million new housing units are built each year, but population growth, demolition of old structures, migration to other sections of the country, and other losses account for almost all of this construction. Even if we were to increase construction by over 30 per cent, a majority of the 8.5 million substandard units would still be standing by 1970.

It is clear that we cannot adequately rehouse America by existing methods. This can only be done, we believe, if advanced production techniques are introduced and combined with adequate community planning that fits the single-family house, low-rise multiple units, and high-rise apartments into an integrated and aesthetic design. Advanced production techniques need not, as some fear, promote monotony or drabness. By use of imaginative architecture and new technical capabilities, it should be possible to create a human environment of beauty and pleasure. What is lacking is the leadership capable of removing organizational barriers. The federal government, acting with private industries and entrepreneurs, has an opportunity to provide that leadership in several ways:

1. It should actively stimulate research in housing and community development through research grants.

2. It can provide incentive for private industrial research by offering large initial markets in federally supported public housing.

3. It could take the lead in modernizing local building codes and removing obstacles to new technology. The federal government—in consultation with the states, the building industry, and building trades unions—should develop an acceptable model code. It should then give financial aid, insure building loans, and build its own facilities only in those localities that modernize their codes in line with the national model.

4. The creation of mass-production housing and the undertaking of large-scale urban reconstruction will create a new industry and many new jobs. The result should be an increased demand for conventional construction skills. But in the event that new techniques cause certain crafts to suffer, it may be necessary to explore the costs of a federally subsidized system of retraining, severance pay, and retirement costs for technologically displaced building trades workers.

VIII. TECHNOLOGY AND THE WORK ENVIRONMENT

Despite the contributions of technology to higher standards of living, we have not yet found ideal solutions to the monotony and drudgery of some work processes. No one disputes that to the greatest possible extent work should be pleasurable and meaningful; the question is how to achieve this goal. Among the necessary preconditions are sufficient affluence to permit experimentation and an understanding that all human beings do not react in the same way to identical work situations. Beyond that, however, must come the realization that machines can now be designed to serve the needs of those who operate them, and that in this creative synthesis of human and purely productive needs we can achieve not only more efficient production but also more satisfactory personal development. This new approach to the work environment cannot be accomplished by men accustomed to dealing with production methods in traditional ways. We must look to our universities and engineering schools, as well as to industry, to train a new generation of men who view the processes of production and employment as an integrated whole in which men and machines interact with each other.

Humanizing the Environment of Work

We do not propose any plan or blueprint for the "humanizing" of work. No single design is possible. Work becomes more meaningful to people when they can relate to a total process or product and understand their own work in the scheme of the whole. Some people are happier on a job when they have opportunities to mingle and talk to each other; others may prefer to work alone. Within productive limits, workers should have some share in determining work methods and in planning changes, particularly technological ones, that affect their jobs.

Much of this can be justified in simple dollars-and-cents terms. But even when the reorganization of the work process may itself increase costs, it is the recognition of the human needs that is most important. And if productivity in the past has been oriented to an increase in the amounts of goods, some of its savings in the future can be utilized to bring a greater satisfaction in work for the individual.[5]

The Flexible Life Span of Work

In the coming "postindustrial society," a man may have to go through two or three work cycles, or careers, to keep abreast of new technologies and intellectual techniques. We believe that, where possible, periodic opportunities should be extended throughout the work life of all Americans to upgrade their skills, to change careers, and to experiment with new work patterns. To this end, we would specify two objectives:

1. *The flexible work life.* Study should be given to a system that would

[5]Patrick E. Haggerty disassociated himself from this comment.

enable individuals to continue their education by allowing them to "charge off" or earn tax credits for education that is necessary for the development of new skills.[6] When industry is forced to lay off workers temporarily, these intermissions should be used as training and study periods, the costs of which could be met by government grants or by tax credits. In short, adaptability to the technological society will be one of the great needs in coming decades. Government, industry, and labor should begin studying measures that can help achieve that objective.

2. *Flexible retirement.* The idea of a fixed retirement age makes little sense in a society where types of work are so diverse. In certain occupations, notably the intellectual ones, age and its experience is a resource that should not be wasted; in some industries, particularly those requiring heavy work, an age balance weighted toward the older side may be a constant drag on productivity. We need to establish flexibility in the patterns of retirement as in education.

A Single Standard of Pay

We will make one final comment on improving the work environment, and that has to do with the mode of payment for work. The industrial revolution—despite sometimes pious disavowals—did turn labor into a commodity, and no more so than in the practice of paying production workers by the piece or by the hour. (In some cases today they are even paid by the tenth of an hour worked!) By contrast, white-collar workers, technical workers, and administrators are paid by the week, the month, or the year.

Whatever the initial logic for this distinction, the time may be near when it can be brought to an end. So long as it continues the worker cannot feel a sense of full participation in the social enterprise. In the new economy that is emerging, the relative number of blue-collar workers is declining. And with the continued growth of mechanization and automation, it is increasingly difficult to measure the contribution of the single worker. The concept of "the piece" or "the hour" loses meaning where work is a team affair and production processes are continuous.

We believe, therefore, that industry and unions should begin to discuss the questions of paying all workers by the same standard and of extending to blue-collar workers the usual prerogatives (e.g., payment for sick leave and jury duty) that most salaried employees enjoy today. We put

[6]Philip Sporn, Joseph C. Beirne, Patrick E. Haggerty, Albert J. Hayes, and Walter Reuther disassociated themselves from this recommendation.

this forth as an objective, recognizing the many difficulties that stand in the way of its adoption.

IX.   IMPROVING PUBLIC DECISION-MAKING

Given our technological capability and our relatively abundant resources, why have we not been more successful in meeting our human and community needs?

In an effort to improve the means of public decision-making, we propose in this section of our report that the government explore the creation of a "system of social accounts." We argue that the present system of local government is too fragmented to meet pressing urban needs. We suggest that a new intellectual technique known as systems analysis can provide a new approach to government planning. And finally, we propose that the federal government encourage, by demonstration grants and by its own procurement policy, socially desirable technological innovations.

A System of Social Accounts

To improve the means for making public decisions, we propose that the government explore the creation of a "system of social accounts." This system would attempt to measure the social benefits and social costs of investments and services, and thus reflect the true costs of a product or service.

The proposed system of social accounts would begin with a series of social indicators that would provide a broader and more balanced reckoning than we now possess of the meaning of economic progress. It would help us evaluate the use of human resources in four areas:

1. by measuring social costs and net returns of economic innovations;
2. by measuring the incidence of social ills (e.g., crime, family disruption) ;
3. by creating "performance budgets" in areas of defined social needs (e.g., housing, education);
4. by establishing indicators of economic opportunity and social mobility.

The ultimate goal would be a balance sheet useful in clarifying policy choices. It would allow us to record not only the benefits of economic and social change, but also the costs, to see how they are distributed and borne.

The question of which costs should be borne by private industry and which by the community is clearly a matter of public policy. One difficulty in our economic accounting today is that costs generated by one group are frequently borne by another. For example, the community may accept the cost, if only the cost of ugliness, when strip mining operators gouge out a countryside. The community accepts this cost, knowing that the strip mining might not be done at all—to the economic detriment of the community—if the private operator had to restore the appearance of the landscape.

Similarly, certain costs of severance pay or maintenance of an aging labor force on a firm's payroll may be so large as to inhibit the introduction of new machines or production methods; such costs might better be borne by the community than by the firm itself.

By measuring the incidence of social ills, society would become aware of the huge price it pays for crime, juvenile delinquency, and the disruption of the family. For such social ills there are no simple causes, as there are in the case of general unemployment. Yet such ills have measurable effects on the economy. A systematic study of these ills and their costs might suggest possible courses of remedial action.

Under the heading of "performance budgets" one might have, for example, a national housing budget, which would indicate how closely we were approaching the goal of a decent home for every American family. A series of community health indices would tell us how well we were meeting the medical needs of our people.

The indicators of economic opportunity and social mobility would shed light on such things as the progress made by the Negro in attaining equality of educational and economic opportunity.

There are today in the government many sources for the kind of data one would need for social accounting. Other data would have to be developed and gathered in systematic form. While much data gathering is involved, the development of a system of social accounts is primarily a problem of interpretation and synthesis. For that reason we recommend that the Council of Economic Advisors take over the task of trying to develop a system of social accounts.

The Fragmented Nature of Our Government Structure

The proliferation of government, especially at the local level, has given rise to serious problems in the coordination of public programs, in reducing public accountability, in making decisions affecting regional areas, and in contributing to wide disparities between available financial resources and community and human needs.

One consequence of this multiplicity of governments is the continuous deterioration of services in our major cities. The citizenry is aroused to action only when a critical condition develops, and then *ad hoc* measures are invoked. But these only postpone the future reckoning.

If local inaction and impotence continue, more and more power over local decisions will be placed, by default, in the hands of state and federal officials. If this situation is to be avoided, local leaders must take the initiative in experimenting with new ideas and new patterns of government that will begin to meet regional needs.

Systems Approach

Technology is more than machines and mechanisms. For solving the mounting problems of our society, some of which we have just touched on, we shall have to call increasingly on what might be called "intellectual technology." This term encompasses intellectual techniques that have been developing along with computers and sophisticated information processing—such things as systems analysis, simulation, and operations research. Much of this as it applies to social and economic actions has been called "the systems approach."

The approach has two main features. First, objectives are stated clearly in performance terms, rather than in terms of particular technologies or preexisting models. Second, it places emphasis upon the interrelations and interactions within a system. In our cities, for example, we divide the traffic problem from problems of housing, school location, and industry location. Yet clearly, the change in traffic flows and densities will affect residential patterns and industry concentration. In short, what a systems approach implies is comprehensive planning so that we can trace out the relevant effects, progressive and regressive, of any set of choices and decisions. The Commission recommends that government agencies, at the local, state and federal levels, avail themselves of this new intellectual tool.

Federal Promotion of Research and Experiment

One of the most effective ways to improve decision-making would be for the federal government to support the application of technology to social problems. One can envisage, for example, an experiment wherein a single large community was designed from scratch by urban planners, economists, and engineers. European countries provide many interesting examples of such a cooperative effort in the planning and construction of new towns. In the United States such efforts are left almost entirely in the hands of private developers.

A second type of experiment would be to utilize the vast purchasing power of the federal government to set up new standards and promote technological innovations in areas not related to military defense or space technology. In 1964 the federal government purchased directly $34 billion of goods and services, of which $26 billion was spent by the Department of Defense. Almost 15 per cent of the total volume of all building and construction in the U.S. was accounted for by federal procurement.

The Commission believes it would be helpful if the federal government modified its purchasing practices to place primary emphasis on performance criteria rather than on product specifications. This means the government would specify the end result without limiting the design to preexisting products. The effect would be to encourage innovation.

Finally, we propose the expansion of government financial aid to universities to permit them to explore urban problems and develop improved systems to meet community needs. In the past the government has used the universities with magnificent results in the advancement of agriculture, and more recently in the realm of advanced military and space technology.[7] These past achievements suggest a pattern that could be fruitfully exploited in solving urban problems.

The Generation and Transfer of Technology

The evidence is overwhelming that the infusion of new technology speeds the rate of economic growth. It is evident that increases in GNP are related to expenditures for research and development (R and D). In 1965 a total of about $21 billion was devoted to R and D, of which about $15 billion was supplied by the federal government. The way in which R and D is spent is important both for the pace of technological advance and for the determination of areas where technology will—and can—be applied.

One would like to be able to answer four questions about R and D expenditures:

1. Is there some optimal limit to the amount spent on R and D?
2. Are there significant imbalances in the present pattern of R and D spending?
3. What can be done to stimulate greater use of R and D by lagging industries?

[7]Philip Sporn disassociated himself from this comment.

4. What kind of federal policy is needed for disseminating technological knowledge to potential users?

Determination of an optimum R and D expenditure is a difficult question. It has been suggested that precise figures should be gathered showing the annual employment of scientific manpower and dollars in relation to the putative national goals they serve. Such a report might provide the framework for a more detailed consideration of the kinds of government expenditures on R and D.

The question of imbalances in existing spending is one that involves political judgments. We feel that important areas—principally housing, transportation, and urban development—have been neglected in federally supported R and D efforts.

It has been argued that certain industries have lagged technologically because of disproportions in R and D spending. Uneven distribution of R and D does not itself indicate inefficient resource allocation among industries. The relevant question is whether it is possible to help potential users who are unable to help themselves. In areas where market criteria cannot generate sufficient incentives for adequate R and D— such as weather forecasting, public health, education—the federal government has a recognized responsibility. And where R and D benefits are insufficiently realized through private capabilities, it is the task of public policy to provide incentives.

The transfer of technologies developed in federal laboratories and agencies for industrial and consumer use requires a more forthright and unified government policy than exists at present. As a minimum we feel that the government has a responsibility for making available for nongovernmental use the results of government-performed research and other research that was substantially funded by the government. The issue is a vexing one, and more detailed study is needed.

Conclusion: The Attainment of National Goals

Ours, like most modern societies, is becoming "future-oriented." We realize that we have to plan ahead. We have to anticipate social change. We need to assess its consequences. We have to decide what policies are necessary to facilitate, or inhibit, possible changes.

Increasingly, technology makes it possible for societies to "invent the future." Given the great resources of this country, we can decide what kind of future we want and work for it. We can spell out our national goals and seek to meet them within the framework of our capacities.

The basic decisions on policy, of course, are made by the President and the Congress operating within the framework of constitutional processes and individual liberties as interpreted by the courts. This system has been the political mainstay of a free society. Our concern is to strengthen this system at a time when social and technological changes begin to confront us ever more directly, and when we need comprehensive means of assessing the consequences of such changes.

Forecasting the future is not a task for government alone. In fact, the concentration of forecasting mechanisms entirely in the hands of government carries the risk of reaching one-sided judgments—and even the suppression of forecasts for political ends.

Along with forecasting there is a need to set national goals and to enlarge the participation of all sectors of society in the broad public debate required to establish priorities. For this reason the Commission, while not endorsing any specific format, feels that some national body of distinguished private citizens representing diverse interests and constituencies and devoted to a continuing discussion of national goals would be valuable. Such a body would be concerned with "monitoring" social change, forecasting possible social trends, and suggesting policy alternatives to deal with them. Its role would not be to invent the future, or even to plan it, but to point out what alternatives are achievable and at what costs.[8]

The Commission, in effect, has been a forum bringing together representatives of industry, labor unions, voluntary associations, universities, and the public in spirited debate—based on factual data where possible —on policy issues that involve a clarification of national goals. None of us, we have learned, is committed to doctrinaire solutions. We begin with a bias to the free market and the free society, but we have also recognized that where the market economy is incapable of providing certain services, public agencies must undertake such functions. Equally, we have agreed that certain communal needs can only be met by federal expenditures, even though the operative activities need not be in the hands of government agencies. But in all this we have become aware of differences in value, and of the need to find some basic agreements in order to be able to carry forward the charge given to us by the President and the Congress.

We must find new means of making our institutions flexible and adaptable while maintaining the mechanism of free choice and of democratic participation.

---

[8]Philip Sporn disassociated himself from this recommendation.

X. SUMMARY OF MAJOR CONCLUSIONS AND RECOMMENDATIONS

The issues discussed in this report are complex and diverse. A brief summary of major conclusions cannot do justice to the report and is certainly not a substitute for the full text with its supporting evidence and argument. Once the text has been read, however, a summary may serve a useful purpose in crystallizing the major points and pointing up the recommendations which have been made. The principal conclusions and recommendations follow:

1. There has been some increase in the pace of technological change. The most useful measure of this increase for policy purposes is the annual growth of output per man-hour in the private economy. If 1947 is chosen as a dividing point, the trend rate of increase from 1909 to that date was 2 per cent per year; from 1947 to 1965 it was 3.2 per cent per year. This is a substantial increase, but there has not been and there is no evidence that there will be in the decade ahead an acceleration in technological change more rapid than the growth of demand can offset, given adequate public policies.

2. The excessive unemployment following the Korean War, only now beginning to abate, was the result of an economic growth rate too slow to offset the combined impact of productivity increase (measured in output per man-hour) and a growing labor force.

3. Since productivity is the primary source of our high standard of living and opportunity must be provided to those of the population who choose to enter the labor force, the growth of demand must assume the blame for and provide the answer to unemployment. But it must be realized that the growth rate required to match rising productivity and labor force growth rates is unprecedented in our history, though not in the history of other industrial economies. There will be a continuing need for aggressive fiscal and monetary policies to stimulate growth.

4. To say that technological change does not bear major responsibility for the general level of unemployment is not to deny the role of technological change in the unemployment of particular persons in particular occupations, industries, and locations. Economic and technological

changes have caused and will continue to cause displacement throughout the economy. Technological change, along with other changes, determines who will be displaced. The rate at which output grows in the total economy determines the total level of unemployment and how long those who become unemployed remain unemployed, as well as how difficult it is for new entrants to the labor force to find employment.

5. Unemployment tends to be concentrated among those workers with little education, not primarily because technological developments are changing the nature of jobs, but because the uneducated are at the "back of the line" in the competition for jobs. Education, in part, determines the employability and productivity of the individual, the adaptability of the labor force, the growth and vitality of the economy, and the quality of the society. But we need not await the slow process of education to solve the problem of unemployment.

6. The outlook for employment and adjustment to change in the next decade depends upon the policies followed. Uneven growth and decline of occupations and industries could, but need not, cause serious difficulties for the economy as a whole. The number of unskilled jobs will not decline, though unskilled jobs will continue to as a proportion of all jobs. Growth patterns in both the economy and the labor force provide an important warning: Unless Negroes and, to a lesser degree, youth, are able to penetrate growing occupations and industries at a more rapid rate than in the past, their high unemployment rates will continue or even rise. Our society must do a far better job than it has in the past of assuring that the burdens of changes beneficial to society as a whole are not borne disproportionately by some individuals.

7. The more adequate fiscal policies of the last two years have proven their ability to lower unemployment despite continued technological change and labor force growth. Economic policy must continue, watchfully but resolutely, to reduce the general unemployment rate. We must never again present the spectacle of wartime prosperity and peacetime unemployment. The needs of our society are such that we should give major attention in our fiscal policies to public investment expenditures.

8. With the best of fiscal and monetary policies, there will always be those handicapped in the competition for jobs by lack of education, skill, or experience or because of discrimination. The needs of our society provide ample opportunities to fulfill the promise of the Employment Act of 1946: "a job for all those able, willing, and seeking to work." We recommend a program of public service employment, providing, in effect, that the government be an employer of last resort, providing work for the "hard-core unemployed" in useful community enterprises.

9. Technological change and productivity are primary sources of our unprecedented wealth, but many persons have not shared in that abundance. We recommend that economic security be guaranteed by a floor under family income. That floor should include both improvements in wage-related benefits and a broader system of income maintenance for those families unable to provide for themselves.

10. To facilitate adjustment to change as well as to improve the quality of life, adequate educational opportunity should be available to all. We recommend compensatory education for those from disadvantaged environments, improvements in the general quality of education, universal high school education and opportunity for fourteen years of free public education, elimination of financial obstacles to higher education, lifetime opportunities for education, training, and retraining, and special attention to the handicaps of adults with deficient basic education.

11. Adjustment to change requires information concerning present and future job opportunities. We recommend the creation of a national computerized job-man matching system which would provide more adequate information on employment opportunities and available workers on a local, regional, and national scale. In addition to speeding job search, such a service would provide better information for vocational choice and alert the public and policy-makers to impending changes.

12. The public employment service is a key instrument in adjustment to technological and economic changes. But it is presently handicapped by administrative obstacles and inadequate resources. We recommend the now federally financed but state-administered employment services be made wholly federal. This would bring them into harmony with modern labor market conditions. Then they must be provided with the resources, both in manpower and funds, necessary to fulfill their crucial role.

13. We recommend that present experimentation with relocation assistance to workers and their families stranded in declining areas be developed into a permanent program.

14. Displacement, technological and otherwise, has been particularly painful to those blocked from new opportunity by barriers of discrimination. The Commission wishes to add its voice to others demanding elimination of all social barriers to employment and advocating special programs to compensate for centuries of systematic denial.

15. Technological and economic changes have differential geographic impacts requiring concerted regional efforts to take advantage of opportunities and avoid dislocation. We recommend that each Federal Reserve Bank provide the leadership for economic development activities in its

region. The development program in each Federal Reserve District should include: (1) a regular program of economic analysis; (2) an advisory council for economic growth composed of representatives from each of the major interested groups within the district; (3) a capital bank to provide venture capital and long-term financing for new and growing companies; (4) regional technical institutes to serve as centers for disseminating scientific and technical knowledge relevant to the region's development; and (5) a federal executive in each district to provide regional coordination of the various federal programs related to economic development.

16. The responsibility of government is to foster an environment of opportunity in which satisfactory adjustment to change can occur. But the adjustments themselves must occur primarily in the private employment relationship. The genius of the private adjustment process is the flexibility with which it accommodates to individual circumstances. Our report suggests areas for consideration by private and public employers, employees, and unions. We also recommend study of a reinsurance fund to protect pension rights and modifications of the investment tax credit to encourage employers to provide appropriate adjustment assistance. We also advocate a positive program by employers and unions to provide compensatory opportunities to the victims of past discrimination and stronger enforcement provisions in civil rights legislation relating to employment. Federal, state, and local governments are encouraged to conduct themselves as model employers in the development of new adjustment techniques.

17. Technology enlarges the capacities of man and extends his control over his environment. The benefits of increased productivity can and should be applied to combinations of higher living standards and increased leisure, improvements in the work environment, increased investment in meeting human and community needs, and assistance to less advantaged nations.

18. As examples of possible applications of new technologies to unmet human and community needs, we recommend improvements in health care, transportation, control of air and water pollution, and housing.

1. To improve health care we recommend: (a) fuller access to diagnostic and patient care facilities by all groups in the population; (b) broader and bolder use of the computer and other new health technologies; (c) increased spread and use of health statistics, information, and indexes; and (d) new programs for training health manpower.

2. To aid the development of an efficient transportation system we recommend federal support of a systems research program directed toward: (a) the

problems of particular multistate regions; (b) the determination of national transportation requirements; and (c) the evaluation of alternative programs.
3. For air pollution control we recommend: (a) enlargement of research efforts to learn and understand the effects of various pollutants on living organisms; and (b) assignment of pollution costs to the sources of pollutants.
4. To control water pollution we recommend the establishment of effective, amply empowered river basin authorities.
5. To encourage improvement in housing technology we recommend: (a) federal stimulation of research; (b) use of federally supported public housing to provide initial markets for new housing technologies; (c) promulgation of a national model building code by making available federal support and insurance of housing and other construction only in those communities which put their building codes in harmony with the national code; and (d) provision of adjustment assistance to any building crafts destroyed by technical change.

19. We also recommend (1) increased use of systems analysis in resolving social and environmental problems, (2) the use of federal procurement as a stimulus to technological innovation through purchasing by performance criteria rather than product specification, (3) provision of federal funds to universities and other organizations for the improvement of research techniques and their experimental application to urban problems, (4) the formation of university institutes integrated with the educational function which would serve as laboratories for urban problem analysis and resources for local communities wanting their advice and services, and (5) increased efforts to make available for nongovernment use results of government-performed or funded research.

20. Finally, we recommend: (1) efforts by employers to "humanize" the work environment by (a) adapting work to human needs, (b) increasing the flexibility of the life span of work, and (c) eliminating the distinction in the mode of payment between hourly workers and salaried employees; (2) exploration of a system of social accounts to make possible assessment of the relative costs and benefits of alternative policy decisions; and (3) continuous study of national goals and evaluation of our national performance in relation to such goals.

Selections from Supplementary Studies

The Commission funded studies related to the employment outlook; the pace of technological change; the impact of technological change on industries, occupations, skill requirements, and hours of work and leisure; measures for adjusting to change; the implication of technological change for education; and the application of technology to unmet human and community needs.[1] Selections from ten of the studies are given here.

At the direction of Congress, the Commission asked the Bureau of Labor Statistics to project manpower requirements by industry and by occupation for the decade ahead. Some observers had posited rising unemployment throughout the years ahead as technology replaced manpower. On this point the Bureau's projections are silent. As the Commission's report stresses, future levels of unemployment depend upon the relationships among economic growth, productivity increases, and labor force growth. Since the first depends so much on current fiscal and monetary policies, it can only be guessed at or assumed. The Bureau assumed an unemployment rate of 3 per cent in 1975, subtracted that figure from the projected labor force, then distributed the resultant employment by industry and occupation. Total employment would rise 26 per cent under those assumptions. Employment in some industries and occupations would rise faster and some slower, but, significantly, few outside of agriculture would experience actual declines. Perhaps the only real surprise in the projections is that the number of unskilled jobs is not expected to decline over the next decade, though such employment will continue to decline as a proportion of total employment. The projections also warn that unless Negroes are able to penetrate more rapidly into growing job sectors than in the past, the gap between Negro and white unemployment rates will grow wider.

The Commission solicited four studies of the present state and future outlook for the use of computers throughout the economy. The most complete over-all study was that by Paul Armer of the Rand Corporation, reproduced in part here. He shows that the cost of computers is falling rapidly and their use is rising correspondingly. He concludes that "in time computers will be able to carry out any information-processing task that men can do." He recognizes, however, that technical and economic feasibility are different things, and what can be done will not necessarily be done. He rejects "the radical view that computers and automation, manned by a small percentage of the available work force, will produce a glut of goods to services."

Measuring the pace of technological change is a difficult task which has not yet been done satisfactorily. The common practice is to use changes in output per man-hour. Since output per man-hour is computed by dividing man-hours worked into total output at two points in time, it measures the impact of all factors affecting productivity. It measures not change itself, but the impact of change, technological and otherwise. However, as long as the concern is employment and unemployment, output per man-hour is the relevant measure. Technological change itself is a complex phenomenon consisting of discovery, application, and diffusion of an idea. If that process could be measured and averaged for the whole economy at different points in time, the pace of technological change could be measured directly.

Frank Lynn measured the time lapse from invention through commercial application to adoption by major portions of an industry for twenty different innovations occurring over the past sixty years. He concluded that the time involved had shortened but was still substantial. Those technological innovations "that will have a significant impact during the 1970–75 period are already at least in a readily identifiable state of commercial development."

No other industry in the United States has felt the disemployment impact of technological change to the extent agriculture has. Further disemployment is yet to come. The Commission undertook a number of industry impact studies, but only selections from the agriculture study are used here. Walter Butcher examines output and productivity trends, identifies their sources, and concludes that if output per man-hour on all farms was equal to that on efficiently organized farms, the present output could be produced by one sixth the present farm manpower.

Juanita Kreps and Joseph Spengler examine the leisure time possibilities of present rates of productivity increase and economic growth. Their tools are simple arithmetic, but with output per man-hour doubling in less than twenty-five years, the results are startling. By 1985, if present trends continue, the average American can choose between a $5800 per capita GNP and a twenty-two-hour workweek, a twenty-five-week vacation or an extra seventeen and a half years in school.

The choice is not a new one, though the magnitude is. We have always taken our productivity and growth partly in income and partly in leisure. The long-term trend has been to take two thirds in income and one third in leisure. However, despite speculations about growing leisure, we seem to be becoming more income-oriented. During the past twenty years the split in the United States has been nine tenths to income increases and only one tenth to leisure.

Myron Joseph, author of the article "Hours of Work Issues," has pointed out, however, that this change in the income-leisure choice may be more apparent than real. When the workweek was very long, reduction in hours may have raised productivity sufficiently to prevent any fall in output and real income. He doubts that this is true at the present average workweek. Joseph examines the possibilities of reducing unemployment through shorter hours of work, including by such means as shortening the standard workweek, increasing overtime penalties, and eliminating moonlighting. Joseph concludes that none of these measures can be effective unless workers are willing to accept lower real incomes, not only sharing unemployment but sharing paychecks.

The most publicized of the Commission's recommendations was the guaranteed family income. Others have made similar recommendations before, but most of these have been offered as an answer to cybernation —visualized as a computer directing an automated assembly line. Their argument has been that our technology will become so productive that full employment will become impossible, and we will have to settle for guaranteed incomes with full unemployment as a goal.[2] The Commission specifically rejected this view, yet made a similar recommendation. Its reason was simply concern for the problems of the poor. Poverty has little to do with technology and automation. Rather, the Commission said, the relationship is that the wealth made available through technology can be shared to reduce or eliminate poverty.

Sar Levitan evaluated for the Commission the present programs designed, at least in part, to aid the poor, and explored a number of

[2]Robert Theobold, ed., *The Guaranteed Income* (Garden City, New York: Doubleday & Company, Inc., 1966) .

current alternative proposals. He agreed that present programs tended to be both niggardly and capricious but thought the political possibilities of reforming and strengthening them were more realistic than the likelihood of new departures. He was also of the view that money alone could not meet the needs of the poor. Social services must be made available of types which the poor might not choose or have available to them if left to their own devices. He advocated with particular forcefulness reduction in family size, aid to impoverished children, work relief, and public housing. The Commission agreed with his premises in advocating strengthening of existing programs, but rejected his advice on advocating a guaranteed income with the negative income tax as the most attractive approach.

Concern for the impact of automation in the United States grew in a period of unemployment. How are the same phenomena viewed from a full employment vantage point? Jack Stieber visited a number of Western European countries searching for an answer. He found the Europeans placing a higher priority on full employment and less concerned for price stability than we. He found them without fear of general unemployment, but he did not find them less concerned with the displacement impact of technological change. American unions are ahead of their European counterparts in achieving job security and adjustment provisions through collective bargaining. Western European employers assume a greater social obligation for providing continuous employment than do American employers. European employers accept greater government intervention in the labor market, and European governments are much more generous in their aids to displaced workers. In part this appears to be an attempt to make unemployment costless in order to reduce opposition to change.

Space does not allow inclusion of examples of four whole areas in which the Commission solicited studies: education, the availability of technological solutions to pressing environmental problems, the applicability of the systems approach to such problems and the "state of the art" of public planning through modeling, simulation, and gaming techniques.

Industrial and Occupational Manpower Requirements, 1964-75

Bureau of Labor Statistics, U.S. Department of Labor

Assuming a labor force of 94.1 million workers in 1975, 2.7 million persons in the Armed Forces, and a 3 per cent unemployment rate, total employment requirements in the United States in 1975 will be 88.7 million, an increase of 26 per cent over the 70.4 million workers employed in 1964.

Despite the over-all increase of more than one quarter in total manpower requirements, not all industries are expected to share equally, if at all, in this anticipated growth, and major changes in the industrial distribution of employment are expected by 1975. Manpower needs in agriculture are expected to continue to decline between 1964 and 1975, even under conditions of a generally full employment economy.

In contrast to the decline in agricultural manpower needs, the projections for 1975 show a rise in total manpower needs in the nonfarm economy of nearly one third (30 per cent). By 1975 nonfarm manpower requirements are expected to increase by more than 19 million over the 65.6 million workers employed in 1964. Most of the increased nonfarm manpower needs will be in wage and salary employment, which is projected to rise at a slightly faster rate than total nonfarm employment. Requirements for nonfarm wage and salary workers are expected to rise from 56.1 million in 1964 to 73.4 million in 1975. The number of other workers (domestics and self-employed and unpaid family workers) is expected to increase over the eleven-year period also, but at a somewhat slower rate. By 1975 the number of these workers needed may reach 11.5 million, a 21 per cent increase over the 9.5 million employed in 1964.

The rate of job growth will continue to be higher in the service-producing industries than in the goods-producing industries. Employment in the goods-producing industries—manufacturing, construction and mining—rose 13 per cent between 1947 and 1964, or from 18.5 million to 20.9 million. Significant gains in productivity resulting from automation and other technological developments have permitted large increases in output in the goods-producing industries without corresponding increases in employment.

Between 1964 and 1975 manpower requirements in the goods-producing sector (excluding agriculture) are expected to increase by about 17 per cent to 24.6 million. The projected increase in manpower requirements in the construction industry (37 per cent) contrasts with a slight decline in mining (of about 3 per cent). Manpower requirements in manufacturing are expected to rise by about 14 per cent, or at half the rate of increase for the economy as a whole. In agriculture (not included in the above discussion of the goods-producing industries), employment is expected to fall by about 21 per cent.

Requirements in the service-producing industries—transportation and public utilities; trade; finance, insurance, and real estate; services and miscellaneous industries; and government—are expected to continue the rapid increase of the post-World War II period, when the number of workers on the payrolls of these industries increased 46 per cent, from 25.4 million in 1947 to 37.2 million in 1964.

Over the 1964–75 decade manpower requirements in the service-producing industries are expected to increase by 38 per cent, reaching 51.3 million in 1975. The largest increase in manpower requirements in the service-producing sector is expected to be in government, nearly all in state and local government. Greater-than-average increases are also expected in the service and miscellaneous industries group (a growth of 43 per cent), trade (33 per cent), and finance, insurance, and real estate (26 per cent). The number of jobs in transportation and public utilities will show a relatively small increase by 1975.

The industrial composition of the economy will change significantly in the years ahead as a result of the differential rates of growth projected for industries. Government and the service and miscellaneous industries will increase sharply as a proportion of total industry employment. Other industries whose relative importance will increase are construction and trade. On the other hand, the relative importance of manufacturing and transportation and public utilities will decline slightly. Continued sharp declines in the proportion they represent of total requirements will take place in mining and in agriculture.

Table 1. Employment of Nonagricultural Wage and Salary Workers,
by Industry, 1964, and Projected Requirements, 1975[1]
(In thousands)

	Actual 1964 employment	Projected 1975 requirements	Per cent change
Total	58,156	75,875	30
Agriculture	4,761	3,745	21
Mining	633	620	(2)
Contract construction	3,056	4,190	37
Manufacturing	17,259	19,740	14
Durable goods	9,813	11,500	17
Ordnance and accessories	247	250	(2)
Lumber and wood products, except furniture	603	550	−9
Furniture and fixtures	406	510	26
Stone, clay, and glass products	612	675	10
Primary metal industries	1,231	1,290	5
Fabricated. metal products	1,187	1,460	23
Machinery	1,606	2,050	28
Electrical equipment and supplies	1,548	2,000	29
Transportation equipment	1,605	1,730	8
Motor vehicles and equipment	755	800	6
Aircraft and parts	604	575	−5
Instruments and related products	369	510	38
Miscellaneous manufacturing industries	399	475	19
Nondurable goods	7,446	8,240	11
Food and kindred products	1,746	1,665	−5
Tobacco manufacturers	89	80	−10
Textile-mill products	891	880	(2)
Apparel and related products	1,302	1,525	17
Paper and allied products	625	775	24
Printing, publishing, and allied products	951	1,100	16
Chemicals and allied products	877	1,125	28
Petroleum refining and related industries	183	160	−13
Rubber and miscellaneous plastic products	434	580	34
Leather and leather products	348	350	(2)
Transportation and public utilities	3,947	4,425	12
Trade, wholesale and retail	12,132	16,150	33
Finance, insurance, and real estate	2,964	3,725	26
Services and miscellaneous	8,569	12,275	43
Total government	9,595	14,750	54
Federal government	2,348	2,525	8
State and local government	7,248	12,225	69

[1]Includes self-employed and unpaid family workers.
[2]Projections assume an unemployment rate of 3 per cent in 1975.
[3]Less than 3 per cent.
NOTE: Because of rounding, sums of individual items may not equal totals.

Projections of Occupational Requirements in 1975

Significant changes have taken place and can be expected to continue to take place in the occupational structure of the U.S. labor force. One of the important changes of the post-World War II period has been the much greater growth in the number of workers in white-collar and service occupations as compared with manual workers, and especially the very large increase in the number and proportion of professional and high-level managerial workers. Employment of white-collar workers rose by more than one half (54 per cent) between 1947 and 1964, rising from less than 20.2 million to more than 31.1 million. Employment of service workers also rose substantially, growing from 6.0 million to 9.3 million, an increase of 55 per cent. At the same time, employment of blue-collar workers increased much less rapidly, increasing about 8 per cent, from 23.6 million to 25.5 million. The number of farm workers actually declined, falling from 8.1 million in 1947 to 4.4 million in 1964, a drop of 45 per cent.

Looking ahead, an increase of nearly two fifths for white-collar jobs over the next decade is indicated. Among white-collar occupations, the most rapid increase in requirements will be for professional and technical workers, which may grow twice as rapidly (54 per cent) as the average for all workers. Requirements for clerical workers are also expected to increase rapidly, rising by nearly two fifths, and sales workers by nearly one third. The demand for managers and officials is expected to rise somewhat more slowly, increasing less than one fourth between 1964 and 1975.

Requirements for blue-collar workers are expected to rise by one sixth between 1964 and 1975. Among the blue-collar workers, the most rapid increase in requirements will be for craftsmen, a rise of somewhat more than one fourth, or about the average rate of increase for total employment as a whole. Requirements for operatives will increase more slowly, by about a seventh, and little change is expected in the demand for laborers.

A more than one fifth decline in requirements is anticipated for farmers and farm workers.

As a result of these differential rates of growth, the occupational composition of the nation's employment will be different in 1975 than it was in 1964. The major changes will be in the proportions of professional and technical workers, service workers, and clerical workers, all of which are expected to rise significantly, and in the proportions of farm workers, operatives, and nonfarm laborers, which will decline as a proportion of

Table 2. Major Occupational Groups of Workers, Actual 1964 Employment
and Projected 1975 Requirements
(Numbers in thousands)

Occupational group	1964 Employment		Projected 1975 Requirements		Per cent change, 1964–75
	Number	Per cent	Number	Per cent	
Total, All occupational groups	70,357	100.0	88,700	100.0	26
White-collar workers	31,125	44.2	42,800	48.3	38
Professional and technical	8,550	12.2	13,200	14.9	54
Managers, officials, and proprietors	7,452	10.6	9,200	10.4	23
Clerical workers	10,667	15.2	14,600	16.5	37
Sales workers	4,456	6.3	5,800	6.5	30
Blue-collar workers	25,534	36.3	29,900	33.7	17
Craftsmen and foremen	8,986	12.8	11,400	12.8	27
Operatives	12,924	18.4	14,800	16.7	15
Nonfarm laborers	3,624	5.2	3,700	4.2	(1)
Service workers	9,256	13.2	12,500	14.1	35
Farm workers	4,444	6.3	3,500	3.9	−21

1 Less than 3 per cent.
NOTE: Projections assume a 3 per cent level of unemployment in 1975. Per cents do not add to totals due to rounding.

total employment. The remaining occupational groups will be roughly the same proportion in 1975 as they were in 1964.

Factors Affecting Occupational Employment Patterns

EFFECTS OF CHANGING TECHNOLOGY

Although many factors other than technological changes have had and will continue to have a significant impact on the occupational structure of the labor force, technological change is nonetheless a major determinant of occupational employment shifts. However, technology is inextricably woven with the other factors influencing employment, and the impact of technology itself is often hard to distinguish.

One impact of technological change on industry occupational patterns can be seen most clearly in industries which are declining in employment. In these industries the greatest decreases in employment have usually taken place among laborers and others in the least skilled groups.

One example is the *railroad industry*, which, under the impact of changes in technology, in the scale of operations, and in product mix, showed both very substantial declines in total employment and significant alterations in occupational composition over the thirteen-year period 1947 through 1960. During this time the diesel engine completely supplanted the steam locomotive, and there were substantial technical improvements in the method of maintaining track and roadbed. At the same time, passenger traffic declined substantially, and freight traffic remained reasonably stable.

The effect of these changes is clearly reflected in the occupational composition of the industry. Employment dropped by more than 40 per cent between 1947 and 1960, for a net loss of nearly 572,000 jobs. However, maintenance-of-way employment dropped by 55 per cent, with the 69 per cent decline in unskilled section hands (who did common labor on the tracks but were replaced by mobile-powered units that made repairs while moving slowly over the track) being offset to some extent by the 47 per cent increase in the number of semiskilled portable equipment operators. Because diesel-electric locomotives require much less repair work than steam locomotives, skilled workers in repair employment dropped by 35 per cent. Boilermakers were the hardest hit craft; their number declined by 82 per cent. On the other hand, employment of electrical workers increased by 15 per cent. Other occupational groups had smaller declines than the 40 per cent drop in the industry as a whole. Professional, clerical, and general office employees declined by only 27 per cent (affected to some extent by the introduction of electronic data processing) and executives declined by only 1 per cent. The net effect of these occupational changes was that executive and office workers increased as a proportion of total employment, and unskilled workers and some maintenance crafts decreased.

The *lumber and wood products* industry is an example of a growing industry in which the number of unskilled jobs declined as mechanized equipment was installed. Employment dropped by more than 180,000 during the 1950–60 period, an average of about 2 per cent per year. At the same time, output rose considerably, owing mainly to the use of faster and more powerful labor-saving machinery such as high-speed handling, sawing, sorting, and stacking equipment. Woodchoppers and unskilled lumbermen decreased significantly between 1950 and 1960, while operators of portable spars, mechanical lumberjacks, and loading and other equipment increased.

In *banking*, technological changes have affected the occupational structure in still another way. Occupational patterns changed rapidly as this fast-growing industry expanded its use of electronic data-processing equipment. The sharpest reductions in manpower requirements for a given volume of work were in the demand deposit sector, where the needs for bookkeepers, proof and transit clerks, and many other routine clerical workers were reduced substantially through the use of magnetic ink character recognition, electronic bookkeeping machines, and full-scale computer systems. On the other hand, among the new jobs created were reader-sorter operator, check encoder or inscriber, control clerk, and keypunch operator; a few new jobs for programers and systems analysts were created at the professional and technician level. About half the people employed in banking—tellers, secretaries, typists, switchboard operators, officers, and professional workers—were not markedly affected by technological change, and their employment continued to rise as banks increased their facilities and added new services.

Examples of the contrasting effects of technology are shown in the changing occupational distributions of the petroleum and baking industries. (See Table 3.) In the *petroleum refining industry*, between 1950 and 1960 laborers decreased in number and proportion, whereas craftsmen and professional workers increased. The increase in employment of craftsmen resulted largely from the growing amount of maintenance needed in the highly instrumented and automated petroleum refining processes. Employment of technicians increased because of the greater utilization of automated and computerized systems.

In the *baking industry*, on the other hand, the biggest increase in the proportion of total employment occurred among sales workers and operatives, whereas craftsmen declined as a proportion of the total. The decline in the relative importance of craftsmen reflected changes in technology, such as the introduction of continuous mixing units and modernized ovens in which products are baked while passing through the oven on a conveyor. In addition, because new methods were developed to freeze perishable items, they were produced in much larger quantities, contributing to the reduction in the relative number of skilled bakery workers required. The increase in sales workers was related to the greater number of driver-salesmen required to handle the much larger volume of bakery products. The increase in proportion of semiskilled workers resulted to a great extent from the large expansion in the number of truckdrivers—more than offsetting the decrease in operatives needed because of the introduction of automatic slicing, packaging, and other machines.

Change in technology in the *telephone industry* resulted in an occupational shift different from those previously described. As Table 4 shows, the greatest shift was the decrease in the proportion of telephone operators and other clerical workers resulting from the conversion from manual systems to automatic dial services for local and long-distance calls, and the introduction of automatic timing and billing services. At the same time, linemen, telephone installers, and repairmen increased because of the growing number of telephones as well as the complexity and growing volume of telephone services.

Table 3. Changes in Occupational Employment in the Petroleum Refining and Bakery Industries, 1950–60

Occupation	Bakeries		Petroleum Refining	
	1950	1960	1950	1960
Total employed (in thousands)	267.0	362.1	257.2	252.7
Total per cent	1 100.0	1 100.0	1 100.0	1 100.0
Professional and technical	0.8	0.6	14.9	16.2
Managers, officials, and proprietors	6.6	6.1	5.9	6.0
Clerical workers	8.5	8.5	17.5	18.1
Sales workers	6.7	9.9	2.1	2.2
Craftsmen and foremen	31.7	27.4	21.7	23.7
Operatives	39.5	41.5	26.3	26.3
Service workers	3.1	3.0	2.3	1.7
Laborers	3.1	2.9	9.2	5.9

1Base used in computing per cents was the employed less the number not reporting occupations.
SOURCE: Department of Commerce, Bureau of the Census.

Table 4. Changes in Occupational Employment in the Telephone Industry, 1950–60

Occupation	1950	1960
Total employed (In thousands)	594.8	692.5
Total per cent	1 100.0	1 100.0
Professional and technical	4.9	6.5
Managers, officials, and proprietors	3.7	5.4
Clerical workers	62.5	55.5
Telephone workers	(44.2)	(31.8)
Sales workers	.3	1.1
Craftsmen and foremen	24.9	28.6
Linemen and servicemen	(22.0)	(25.5)
Operatives	1.2	.7
Service workers	1.6	1.7
Laborers	.8	.5

1Base used in computing per cents was the total employed less the number not reporting occupations.
SOURCE: Department of Commerce, Bureau of the Census.

Perhaps the most dramatic impact of technological change on employment has taken place on the farm. As a result of increased mechanization, the use of scientific methods, chemical fertilizers, better seeds, and the like, productivity in *agriculture* has increased much more rapidly than in most industries. Employment has declined despite the need to grow more food for the increasing population. Furthermore, the occupational structure of farm employment has been sharply affected. For example, between 1950 and 1960 farmers and farm laborers decreased by about 40 per cent, but the number of professional workers in agriculture rose by about 20 per cent—such workers include airplane pilots (for crop dusting), scientists, foresters, accountants, and veterinarians.

The above illustrative descriptions of the impact of technological developments on selected industries should not obscure the fact that the effect of technological change on the occupational structure of most industries is extremely complex and cannot be traced easily. For the most part, technological innovations are not adopted extensively in an industry or an individual plant at any single time. Instead, they are often adopted piecemeal in the form of a great many minor changes introduced in one establishment and then in another, and often in a gradual way within an establishment. In view of the multitude of small changes having a different effect on the occupational pattern of an industry, it is extremely difficult, particularly without comprehensive current data on changing occupational employment patterns in individual industries, to determine the net effect of all technological changes.

FACTORS OTHER THAN TECHNOLOGICAL CHANGE

In addition to technological change, there are several other major factors affecting occupational employment patterns. The most important of these other factors are the different rates of employment growth among industries resulting from shifts in the distribution of income and changing patterns of consumption; growth in population and its changing age distribution; government policy and federal expenditures; institutional factors such as union-management relationships and practices; and the relative supply of persons in different occupations. These and other factors are discussed below.

Population Growth. One of the major determinants of occupational change is growth in population and its changing age distribution. Rapid increases in population bring about sharp rises in the demand for goods and services of all kinds, and result in employment increases in industries producing them. As the population grows, there is a concomitant increase in the demand for the products needed to feed, clothe, and house the increased numbers of people, and as industry expands its production of goods to meet these needs, employment often expands also. Similarly, the growing population requires increased services, which results in a rise in volume of business in service-producing industries, and therefore in the demand for workers such as barbers, hairdressers, lawyers, bankers, and medical personnel. The increasing urbanization of the population is responsible for the expansion of state and local government employment in order to provide the public services needed for urban living, such as those provided by firemen and policemen. Often, many of these occupations increase nearly in direct proportion to the increase in population.

In addition to the impact of over-all population growth, the changing age distribution of the growing population plays a major role in influencing employment growth in some industries and their occupations. For example, a very large part of the increase in professional workers has been due to the changing composition of the population. A greater number of teachers are needed to service the rising number and proportion of school-age children in the population. Similarly, the increasing number of older persons in the population tends to bring about an even greater increase in demand for medical personnel.

Government Policy and Federal Expenditures. Government policy and federal, state, and local expenditures play a major role not only in determining the occupational composition of employment, but in providing and stimulating over-all employment. It is estimated, for example, that nearly 3 million workers are currently engaged in federally sponsored defense-related activities. Expenditures for education increase not only the employment of teachers, but of the construction workers and others needed to build, maintain, and administer the schools. Similarly, occupations such as social workers, doctors, nurses, highway engineers, and many others are affected by the size and direction of government expenditures.

Of the federal programs, defense and space activities have had the greatest effect on the occupational distribution of employment in the United States. Large and rising government expenditures for research and development, for example, are in great part responsible for the dramatic increase in the demand for scientists, engineers, and technicians.

Employment Growth Among Industries. The different rates of employment growth among industries, as affected by the factors described above, may have been the most important single factor determining the occupational distribution of employment in the United States.[1] An examination of industry employment trends indicates that the very large increases in white-collar employment in the economy as a whole have resulted from the greater-than-average growth in industries employing large numbers of these workers—for example, state and local government, finance, insurance, and real estate, trade, and business and professional services—coupled with the much slower growth in industries in which smaller numbers of white-collar workers are employed—mining, manufacturing, and transportation. Of course, differences in industry employment growth also reflect shifts in the distribution of income and changes in patterns of consumption, which in turn may bring about changes in the demand for products of particular industries, and hence employment changes. Furthermore, the greater growth of some industries has resulted from technological developments, i.e., new inventions such as television. The rapid growth of the space program is another example of how technological innovations may bring about rapid industry employment growth.

Another example of the importance of industry growth to occupational employment may be found in the recent employment rises in the manufacturing and construction industries resulting from high levels of high-economic activity nationally. Closely related to this recent expansion has been the sharp reversal of the half-decade downtrend in the number of workers employed in blue-collar jobs. Employment in these manual occupations increased by 700,000 between 1962 and 1963 and by over half a million between 1963 and 1964, as contrasted with the decline which totaled 600,000 jobs for the half decade between 1957 and 1962.

Union-Management Relationships and Practices. The occupational pattern of an industry may be influenced greatly by collective bargaining agreements and the relationship between labor and management. The construction industry is a good example of the influence labor-management decisions may have in maintaining occupations nearly intact through decades of technological change. The railroad, longshore, and newspaper industries are other cases where, in general, the influence of unions has been directed toward the maintenance of occupational skills. Union-management decisions are often important enough to have a marked effect on the occupational patterns of the economy as a whole.

Collective bargaining agreements may also have a different type of effect on occupations. For example, union-management agreements pro-

---

[1]Of course, growth of some industries is due to new technology and inventions, and decreases in some industries are due in part to increases in productivity.

viding for early retirements may serve to accelerate the rate of decline of occupations in which employees either are or may become surplus. On the other hand, agreements which provide for shorter working hours (as with truck and bus drivers) or longer holidays (such as in the steel, can, and aluminum industries) may increase or at least maintain the requirements for workers.

Supply and Demand Factors. Scarcities and surpluses among different occupations provide management with the opportunity to engineer the jobs to match in some degree the available supply of workers. For example, when engineers are in short supply, many routine engineering functions are reprogramed to be performed by technicians, and additional technicians are hired to perform these functions. In other cases, a production process or material may be adjusted so as to employ a combination of labor skills different from those in short supply.

OTHER FACTORS

One of the many other nontechnological factors which influence occupational employment is the nation's social climate. Increasing concern with the problems of education, living conditions, health standards, and discrimination result in increased requirements for many occupations such as teachers, guidance counselors, and social workers. These requirements are over and above those created by population growth. Organizational changes and improvement in managerial practices also influence the growth rates of occupations. Mergers and acquisitions of firms often affect many middle-management jobs, as does the streamlining of administrative procedures. More liberal tax conditions, lower corporate tax rates, and new depreciation guidelines also affect occupations in that they may increase the profitability of new machinery and equipment.

Projected Changes in Occupational Requirements as They Relate to Selected Subgroups of Workers

CHANGING OCCUPATIONAL REQUIREMENTS AND EMPLOYMENT
OPPORTUNITIES FOR NONWHITE WORKERS

In recent years nonwhite workers have had unemployment rates about twice as high as those for white workers. The average unemployment rate for nonwhites in 1964 was 9.8 per cent, while for whites it was 4.6 per cent. This disparity reflects, in part, the lower educational levels of nonwhites and their concentration in occupations subject to higher-than-average unemployment rates. They are concentrated disproportionately in laborer occupations—both in industry and on farms—and service occupations, and have lower proportions in white-collar and craft occupations than do white workers.

The occupations in which the greatest number of nonwhites are now employed will be growing more slowly than other occupations over the next ten years. Therefore, if employment opportunities for nonwhites are to improve, or even remain the same, they must continue to gain access to the rapidly growing higher skilled and white-collar occupations.

If the nonwhites were merely to continue holding the same proportion of the jobs in each occupation that they held in 1964—that is, if they were to make no advances in gaining access to the craft and white-collar occupations—the nonwhite share of total employment would decline, simply because of the slower growth of the occupations in which they are concentrated.

Table 5 illustrates what the plight of the nonwhite workers will be by 1975 if they continue to hold the same proportion of the jobs in each occupational group as in 1964. The total number of nonwhites employed in 1975 under these assumptions would be 8,970,000, an increase of about 1.5 million, or 20 per cent, as compared to 1964. This rate of increase in employment would be slower than that of white workers, whose employment is projected, under this assumption, to rise by about 27 per cent.

The implications of this slower growth in employment for unemployment among nonwhites may be seen by comparing this estimate of their employment in 1975 with the nonwhite labor force projected for that year. Preliminary projections of the latter show a total nonwhite labor force of about 11 million in 1975. Assuming that the same number of nonwhites will be in the Armed Forces in 1975 as in July 1963 (about 200,000), we would derive a nonwhite civilian labor force of 10.8 million. If approximately 9 million were employed, as computed above, the remainder—1.8 million—would be unemployed—*an unemployment rate of about 17 per cent—five times the unemployment rate for the whole labor force* assumed in the projections of employment.

Actually nonwhites have made some gains in recent years in shifting to the higher skilled and faster growing occupations. As shown in Table 6, nonwhites increased their share of the jobs in the white-collar occupations from 3.1 per cent in 1954 to 4.5 per cent in 1964. The gains took place in each of the major occupation groups of white-collar workers; the gain was steady over the whole ten-year period in clerical occupations, but among professional, sales, and managerial occupations the greatest increase took place after 1958.

Table 5. Illustrative Projections of Employment of Nonwhite Workers in 1975, on the Assumption That They Will Retain the Same Share of Employment in Each Occupation as in 1964

(In thousands)

Occupational group	Employment, 1964			Hypothetical employment, 1975		
	Total	Non-white	Non-white as a per cent of total	Total[1]	Non-white	Non-white as a per cent of total
Total, all occupations	70,400	7,480	10.6	88,700	8,970	10.1
Professional, technical, and kindred workers	8,600	500	5.8	13,200	770	5.8
Managers, officials, and proprietors (excluding farm)	7,500	190	2.6	9,200	240	2.6
Clerical and kindred workers	10,700	570	5.4	14,600	780	5.3
Sales workers	4,500	140	3.1	5,800	180	3.0
Craftsmen, foremen, and kindred workers	9,000	530	5.8	11,400	670	5.9
Operatives and kindred workers	12,900	1,520	11.8	14,800	1,740	11.8
Laborers (excluding farm and mine)	3,600	970	26.9	3,700	1,990	26.9
Service workers	9,300	2,410	26.0	12,500	3,080	24.7
Farm workers	4,400	650	14.6	3,500	520	14.8

[1]Total employment has been projected earlier in this report.

NOTES: (1) Because of rounding, sums of individual items may not equal totals. (2) Total employment is rounded to the nearest 100,000, and nonwhite employment is rounded to the nearest 10,000; the percentages are derived from unrounded data. (3) The computations were done separately for the following occupational categories: medical and other health; teachers, except college; other professional and technical; managers, officials, and proprietors; stenographers, typists, and secretaries; other clerical workers; retail trade sales workers; other sales workers; carpenters; construction craftsmen, except carpenters; mechanics and repair men; metal craftsmen, except mechanics; other craftsmen and kindred workers; foremen, not elsewhere classified; drivers and deliverymen; other operatives; nonfarm laborers; private household workers; service workers, except private household; farmers and farm managers; and farm laborers and foremen.

There was a more modest gain in the nonwhite share of employment in blue-collar occupations—from 10.9 per cent in 1954 to 11.8 per cent in 1964. This reflected a slight decline in their share of laborer jobs, a slight gain among operatives, and a substantial gain among craft jobs.

In service occupations, where nonwhites have traditionally had a

Table 6. *Nonwhite Employed Workers as a Per Cent of Total Employment in Each Major Occupation Group, 1954–64*

Occupational group	1954[2]	1955[2]	1956[2]	1957[2]	1958	1959	1960	1961	1962	1963	1964
Total, all occupations	10.3	10.2	10.3	10.4	10.2	10.3	10.6	10.4	10.5	10.5	10.6
Professional, technical, and kindred workers	3.9	3.9	3.7	3.8	3.8	4.3	4.4	4.1	4.6	5.3	5.8
Managers, officials, and proprietors (excluding farm)	2.1	2.3	2.2	2.1	2.3	2.3	2.5	2.5	2.5	2.6	2.6
Clerical and kindred workers	3.7	3.8	3.8	4.4	4.3	4.4	5.2	5.4	5.1	5.1	5.4
Sales workers	2.3	2.0	1.8	1.9	2.1	2.1	2.6	2.5	2.6	3.0	3.1
Craftsmen, foremen, and kindred workers	3.8	4.0	4.2	4.4	4.5	4.5	4.9	4.9	4.9	5.2	5.8
Operatives and kindred workers	10.7	10.6	11.2	11.3	11.3	11.2	11.8	11.9	11.7	11.8	11.8
Laborers (excluding farm and mine)	27.5	27.6	26.7	27.3	26.6	27.7	26.4	25.7	27.0	26.2	26.9
Service workers	29.0	28.6	28.2	28.2	27.6	26.7	26.8	26.3	26.4	26.3	26.0
Farm workers	15.3	14.3	14.9	15.3	14.9	15.5	16.2	15.7	16.1	15.3	14.6

[1] Data through 1956 have not been adjusted to reflect changes in the definitions of employment and unemployment adopted in January 1957.

[2] Averages based on data for January, April, July, and October.

SOURCES: Bureau of the Census and Bureau of Labor Statistics

Table 7. *Illustrated Projections of Employment of Nonwhite Workers in 1975, on the Assumption That Their Share of Employment in Each Occupation Changes at the Same Annual Rate as in the 1958–64 Period*

Occupational group	Employment, 1958			Employment, 1964			Hypothetical employment 1975		
	Total	Nonwhite	Nonwhite as a per cent of total	Total	Nonwhite	Nonwhite as a per cent of total	Total	Nonwhite	Nonwhite as a per cent of total
Total, all occupations	64,000	6,520	10.2	70,400	7,480	10.6	88,700	10,000	11.3
Professional, technical, and kindred workers	7,000	260	3.8	8,600	500	5.8	13,200	1,180	8.9
Managers, officials, and proprietors, (excluding farm)	6,800	150	2.3	7,500	190	2.6	9,200	300	3.2
Clerical and kindred workers	9,100	390	4.3	10,700	570	5.4	14,600	1,050	7.2
Sales workers	4,200	90	2.1	4,500	140	3.1	5,800	290	5.0
Craftsmen, foremen, and kindred workers	8,500	380	4.5	9,000	530	5.8	11,400	880	7.7
Operatives and kindred workers	11,400	1,300	11.3	12,900	1,520	11.8	14,800	1,900	12.8
Laborers (excluding farm and mine)	3,600	960	26.6	3,600	970	26.9	3,700	960	25.9
Service workers	7,800	2,150	27.6	9,300	2,410	26.0	12,500	2,960	23.7
Farm workers	5,600	830	14.9	4,400	650	14.6	3,500	500	14.2

See Notes in Table 5.

disproportionately large share of the jobs, their share decreased moderately, from 29 to 26 per cent in the 1954–64 period.

Nonwhites moved out of farm occupations in roughly the same proportions as did white workers over the ten-year period. The nonwhite share of farm employment continued at about the same level, between one sixth and one seventh of the total. In 1964 it was 14.6 per cent, slightly below the 15.3 per cent of 1954.

If these trends continue, the effect would be to increase total nonwhite employment and to reduce the gap between white and nonwhite unemployment. To illustrate this, a computation of nonwhite employment in 1975 was made on the assumption that the changes in the period 1958 to 1964 in the proportion of jobs in each occupation filled by nonwhites would continue at the same annual rate in the period 1964 to 1975 (Table 7). The period since 1958 was chosen because some of the major changes have occurred since then. Under this assumption, nonwhite employment would be about 10 million in 1975, a gain of about 2.5 million, or about one third, as compared to a little more than 25 per cent gain in employment of white workers. With the same nonwhite civilian labor force estimated above—10.8 million—this would leave almost 800,000 nonwhite unemployed, *an unemployment rate of 7.5 per cent—two and one half times as high as the projected 3 per cent unemployment rate for the whole labor force.* Thus, the present disparity in unemployment rates between whites and nonwhites would still remain in 1975 if the nonwhites continue to gain access to the higher skilled jobs at the same rate as in the past eight years.

In summary, the effect of the projected shifts in the occupational requirements of the U.S. economy on employment opportunities for nonwhites is such that *they will have to gain access to the rapidly growing higher skilled and white-collar occupations at a faster rate than they have in the past eight years if their unemployment rate is to be brought down toward the same level as that of their white fellow citizens.* In part, this is a matter of providing educational and training opportunities; in part, of reducing racial discrimination in hiring.

CHANGING OCCUPATIONAL REQUIREMENTS AND
EMPLOYMENT OPPORTUNITIES BY AGE

Applying the actual 1964 age distribution of individual occupations to the comparable projected 1975 occupational requirements results in a hypothetical age distribution of 1975 employment which is somewhat different from that of 1964. A comparison of the actual 1964 age distribution and the hypothetical 1975 age distribution indicates that relatively fewer jobs will be available for younger workers and older workers. As Table 8 shows, relative requirements for workers 14–19 years of age would decline from 7.9 per cent of the total (employed civilian labor force) in 1964, to 7.6 per cent in 1975. Similarly, requirements for workers age 55 and over would also decline, falling from 18.1 per cent of the total in 1964 to 17.9 per cent in 1975. These would be offset by somewhat higher proportions in the 25–54 age groups, as the following table shows.

The relative decline in requirements for workers 14 to 19 years of age can be attributed in great part to the projected decline in employment of farm workers. In 1964 a relatively high percentage of farm workers were between 14 and 19 years of age and as requirements for farm workers continue to decline, this age group will be sharply affected.

The relative decline in requirements for workers 55 years and older also apparently results from decreasing employment of farm workers. Increased requirements for managers, officials, and proprietors, which also had relatively large numbers of older workers in 1964, are not expected to be great enough to offset this decline in the number of farm workers.

The implications of these changing patterns of requirements by age emerge more clearly through a comparison of the age distribution of the supply of workers expected to be available in 1975, projected independ-

Table 8. Age Distribution of 1964 Employment and Hypothetical 1975 Requirements

Age	Actual, 1964	Hypothetical, 1975
Number of workers	70,357,000	88,700,000
	Per cent distribution	
Total, all ages	100.0	100.0
14–19	7.9	7.6
20–24	10.4	10.5
25–34	19.1	19.4
35–44	23.0	23.2
45–54	21.5	21.4
55–64	13.9	13.8
65 and over	4.2	4.1

SOURCE: 1964 data are computed from Special Labor Force Report No. 52. "Labor Force and Employment in 1964," *Monthly Review,* April 1965. 1975 estimates are from the Bureau of Labor Statistics.

ently by the Bureau of Labor Statistics.[2] Such a comparison indicates
that some major differences could exist between the hypothetical requirements and the supply of workers by age.

The major difference occurs in the proportion of workers in the
youngest age groups—14–19 and 20–24 years of age. In both these age
groups the relative supply of workers in the labor force in 1975 exceeds
the requirements indicated by the hypothetical 1975 employment based
on the assumption that the age composition of occupations in 1975 will
be the same as obtained in 1964. As Table 9 shows, although nearly
one fourth (23 per cent) of the projected civilian labor force may be
young persons aged 14–24, the hypothetical age distribution of projected
1975 employment requirements indicates that less than one fifth (about
18 per cent) of the requirements will be for workers in this age group.[3]
A similar, though smaller, difference exists for workers 25–34 years of
age, who are expected to comprise 22 per cent of the projected labor force
compared with less than 20 per cent of the hypothetical 1975 requirements. Among workers in the 35–54 age groups—sometimes called the
prime working ages—the comparison shows the opposite effect—a smaller
proportion of workers available (37 per cent of the total civilian labor
force) than are required (45 per cent of the hypothetical requirements).
In the remaining age groups—55–64 and 65 years and older—there appears
to be rough comparability in requirements and supply.

Table 9. Age Distribution of 1975 Civilian Labor Force and Hypothetical
1975 Requirements

Age	Civilian labor force	Hypothetical requirements
	Per cent	
Total, all ages	100.0	100.0
14–19	9.7	7.6
20–24	13.5	10.5
25–34	22.4	19.4
35–44	17.5	23.2
45–54	19.5	21.4
55–64	13.9	13.8
65 and over	3.6	4.1

[2]See Special Labor Force Report No. 49, "Labor Force Projections for 1970–80,"
Monthly Labor Review, February 1965. These projections were adjusted upwards to
reflect the larger labor force under a 3 per cent level of unemployment.

[3]It should be reiterated that actual numbers of persons in these and other age
categories are not directly comparable, since the total of projected requirements
excludes the unemployed workers which are included in the civilian labor force.

A number of possible implications emerge from these projected differences in requirements and supply. One possible implication is that employers may have to lower the minimum age at which they hire workers for particular occupations. Another is that industry patterns of utilization might have to change, with more young workers hired as aids and assistants to the relatively more scarce mature and experienced workers. Perhaps another implication might be that even more young workers than anticipated would delay their entry into the labor market in order to obtain the education and training needed to fill the available jobs. Still another might be that workers would have to be promoted to supervisory or foremen positions at an earlier age than formerly. (It might also mean better opportunities for younger workers to advance to middle-management positions.)

These possible alternatives are by no means the only ones, and by indicating them it is not meant to imply that they are either desirable or likely. They are presented only to illustrate the possible implications of the changing occupational requirements.

Computer Aspects of Technological Change

by Paul Armer, The RAND Corporation

In his excellent book *The Shape of Automation*,[1] Herbert A. Simon suggests that attitudes toward computers and their economic implications have two dimensions—technological and economic.

Like Simon, I am a technological radical and an economic conservative as he defines them, although in each case somewhat closer to the center. That is, with respect to technology, I believe that in time computers will be able to carry out any information-processing task that men can do. However, I believe that many of the problems remaining to be solved are very difficult; i.e., I am not as optimistic as Simon, who foresees computers doing anything man can do, with only minor qualifications and reservations, in our time.

Economically, I reject the radical view that computers and automation, manned only by a small percentage of the available work force, will

[1]Herbert A. Simon, *The Shape of Automation*, (New York: Harper & Row, 1965).

produce a glut of goods and services. Rather, I believe that although computers and automation will contribute to a somewhat accelerated rise in productivity, full employment can be maintained. I further believe that although mankind will find life in the future considerably different, both economically and socially, the change need not be traumatic.

This is not to suggest that I believe that computers and automation are not causing problems requiring economic, social, and political adjustments. They obviously are—and the problems are serious ones. Computers are becoming faster, smaller, and less expensive, and for that reason I foresee the following developments:

COMPUTING POWER WILL BECOME AVAILABLE MUCH THE SAME AS ELECTRICITY AND TELEPHONE SERVICE ARE TODAY

Variously called information-processing networks, information utilities, online time-shared systems, or computer utilities, such systems consist of a number of terminals (input/output devices—today usually a teletype unit or a modified typewriter) connected over communication links (the connection may be permanent or dialed up when needed) to a very high speed computer with a large storage capacity. The central computer devotes a very small period of time to each i/o device in turn. But because the speed of the central computer is so great, each user appears to be receiving the complete attention of the computer.

Computer utilities can be organized in several ways. Large firms may buy the computer system and install terminals within their plant or at branch offices. Multiplant firms may connect all terminals to a single large computer or have several decentralized computers which are connected together. The terminals of many small firms may be connected to the computer of an organization formed to serve those firms. The seller may be a computer service bureau, a commercial bank, a computer manufacturer, a communications supplier, or possibly a large, regulated public utility. Eventually, through the flexibility provided by an adequate communications network, a given terminal could be connected at will to any one of many information utilities.

The communications link introduces a new item into the total cost picture, raising the question that if computers are to become very inexpensive in the future, why not have the computer at hand rather than pay communication costs to a centralized facility? The answer is that over something like the next five years and possibly longer, the relative costs of computers and communications will be such that networks will exist in large numbers. As the cost of storage and CPU's continues to decline, however, it may become less expensive to install some processing and storage capability at the terminal, thus avoiding communication costs. However, at times it will undoubtedly be advantageous to have access to the large "centralized data banks" which will come into existence in the next decade, and thus considerable use will be made of communication links. Consequently, in the 1970s there will probably be much computing power at the terminal itself. The terminal will be connected, when necessary, over a communications network to a central computer system to make available even more computational ability and information of many kinds from large data files.

INFORMATION ITSELF WILL BECOME INEXPENSIVE AND READILY AVAILABLE

As a consequence of information processing becoming inexpensive, and with the existence of information-processing networks, information as a commodity will itself become inexpensive and readily available. For example, a man going from Los Angeles to Chicago on a business trip could quickly learn what flights (of all airlines) leave Los Angeles for Chicago after 5 P.M.; which motels are within five miles of the Chicago airport, and what their characteristics are; and biographical data and credit rating on individuals to be seen. A family needing a new refrigerator could readily get information on available models and might also consult *Consumer Reports* for their latest evaluation of refrigerators.

None of the above will be available next year, and even in ten years some of it may not be truly inexpensive, but the trend is undeniable.

COMPUTERS WILL BECOME EASIER TO USE

Computers are capable of only a comparatively few basic operations—addition, subtraction, multiplication, division, comparison of words or numbers, etc. A list of basic instructions in proper sequence (the program) must be fed into a computer in order for it to do useful work. Early users learned that programing a computer is a difficult, time-consuming, and expensive process, with the cost often exceeding that of the machine time. The most important development reducing this burden has been the introduction of so-called "higher level languages." Rather than writing out a detailed list of instructions in the language of the machine, the user writes the program in a richer language that considerably reduces the number of instructions he has to write and relieves him of concern over many details. The instructions in this higher level language are fed into the computer, and a program in the machine translates them into detailed instructions which the machine can then carry out. While such languages do relieve the user of having to know machine-level language and are extensively used today, they are highly stylized and somewhat difficult to learn. In the next decade, however, further improvements in higher level languages should result in their becoming much easier to learn and to use. For many applications they will permit a user who knows very little about computers to instruct the machine.

The "online" attribute of computer utilities will also make machines easier to use. "Online" means that interaction between user and machine is direct and takes place without perceivable delay. In the past, the delay has been usually at least an hour and more often a day.

ORGANIZATIONS ALREADY UTILIZING COMPUTERS WILL EXPAND FROM
RECORDKEEPING AND ACCOUNTING APPLICATIONS INTO
MANAGEMENT SCIENCE AND DECISION-MAKING

When companies first installed computers, they tended to isolate a given activity, such as payroll or accounts receivable, and develop a computer program for it. Usually, they simply computerized their previous manual procedures or punched-card system, viewing the firm as separable pieces such as sales and manufacturing rather than as an interlocking entity. Next, "integrated data processing" was in vogue; this was based on integrating the various applications into a single data-processing system. Often the old organizational structure of the firm was found to be inappropriate to this approach. Such systems were usually an improvement, but they were still tied to the old concept of supplying historical data for accounting purposes. The information which management really wanted was still not available, and the system gave them little aid in making decisions.

Today the idea is to construct management information systems to provide information for operational decisions rather than for accounting purposes. Such systems are planned around internal computer utilities (although this is not crucial) with fairly elaborate terminals. A manager may sit at a terminal, request information, and have the computer manipulate it for him. Corporate plans can be filed in the computer and compared with actual performance. Simulation models of the firm and its environment will assess alternate strategies; computer programs will be available to optimize manufacturing scheduling, distribution of goods, plant location, etc. With an "online" system using up-to-date data, plans can be revised frequently.

Such utilization of computers permits better use of resources in the form of both labor and capital. In many instances, the increased productivity of capital resources which results may be as important as increased productivity of labor.

When organizations first install a computer, management science often rides piggyback on the computer, sometimes with results far exceeding those of mere computerization. In the early 1950s a water heater manufacturer who was turning out four sizes of heaters in three quality grades bought a small punched-card accounting system. Production was tripled and cost per unit reduced appreciably. But the truth was that the work the machines did could have been done by one or two clerks. Production was affected not by the punched-card system but through the management science introduced by the punched-card salesman for production scheduling and inventory control. Such experiences are not unusual.

This does not imply that the computer is unnecessary for most applications of management science and operations research. In fact, many are impossible without the computer. The point is that the computer often spurs the organization to take the so-called "total systems approach," examining the interplay between all the activities of the company. It forces the organization to ask "Why do we do it that way?" and "What are our goals?" The computer makes the company be systematic, often for the first time. The computer often forces an organization to examine itself to an extent it never did before.

COMPUTER MANUFACTURERS WILL ASSUME MORE OF THE BURDEN OF PROVIDING PACKAGES OF PRETESTED PROGRAMS FOR SPECIFIC APPLICATIONS AND INDUSTRIES

The cost of developing a specific program can be quite high. Further, instruction preparation must be preceded by analysis of the procedure to be mechanized and design of a process to carry it out. In the past, the cost of performing these functions has constituted a barrier to computer use, particularly by small firms. However, to sell equipment to small organizations, computer manufacturers now offer, in addition to machines, packaged pretested programs for specific functional needs (e.g., sorting or inventory control) and to meet the special requirements of a given industry (e.g., hospitals). Similarly, computer service bureaus often develop and sell programs for specific applications.

Packaged programs represent a new force on the pace of technological change. In the past, only large firms could normally afford computer-applied management science and operations research. Their techniques were usually proprietary, and small firms had difficulty keeping up. In fragmented industries with many small producers, no one had the finances to be innovative. But now the computer manufacturer, service bureau, and computer utility are anxious to sell computer capability to small firms and are willing to invest in industry analysis, operations research, and packaged programs. For example, the apparel industry, although the fourth largest manufacturing employer, is made up of many medium-sized firms and has hardly been touched by computers up to the present. Through the more aggressive selling activities of suppliers, computers and management science will be applied extensively to this industry in the next five years.

UTILIZATION OF COMPUTERS WILL BECOME ECONOMICALLY FEASIBLE FOR ALL FIRMS

As computers become less expensive, more firms will be able to afford one on their premises. Service bureaus are available today and economically feasible for many more firms than actually use them. Further, as computer utilities develop, inexpensive computing power will be available in small increments over communication links. Finally, computer manufacturers, service bureaus, or computer utilities will supply packaged computer programs to small firms at little or no cost (i.e., the cost will be buried in charges for computing power).

COMPUTERS WILL BE USED TO CONTROL COMPLETE SYSTEMS

Some years ago, the application of computers to the process industries (e.g., chemical, petroleum, power, and steel) was the subject of much, and as it turned out, rather optimistic speculation. Computers and the necessary instrumentation were too expensive and too unreliable, and the processes themselves were not well understood.

However, much progress has been made in recent years, and as new instrumentation is developed, computer control of complete systems will expand considerably in many types of industries. Computers will be used to control manufacturing processes and, coupled with materials-handling equipment, to provide automatic warehousing. They will also be used for testing and quality control; e.g., to check out an automobile's electrical system before it leaves the assembly line.

COMPUTERS WILL BE USED TO PROCESS PICTORIAL IMAGES AND GRAPHIC INFORMATION

Computers were first used to manipulate numbers in scientific and engineering calculations and later to process alphabetic information for commercial applications. Now they are being used to manipulate pictorial information. In the simplest form of such processing the computer can only record, store, retrieve, and display pictures or drawings; it cannot manipulate the information in the picture or drawing. Nonetheless, such a system has many applications; e.g., a file of engineering drawings or correspondence files. In more advanced systems, the computer can manipulate the pictorial information and perform a wide range of sophisticated processes. For example, an architect can call forth a drawing and add or change lines, specifications, etc., by drawing on a special tablet or on the display. The computer can calculate such things as stresses and can evaluate the design from an engineering standpoint. The computer will not, however, be able to recognize complex patterns for a long time. That is, the computer will not be able to retrieve from storage the plans for the "house with the guest room over the garage," unless, of course, an index to such information had been prepared by humans in advance.

The computer's capability to process images and drawings together with its ability to calculate will revolutionize the designer's work in the next decade by making design less expensive and faster. Such systems are already being used to design such things as automobiles, airplanes, and computer circuits. In automotive design it is estimated that, by using these techniques coupled with numerically controlled machine tools, the present leadtime from initial styling to showroom floor of twenty-eight to thirty months can be cut to ten to twelve months. Such machine aid can, for some applications, even make the design process economical enough to handle custom designed one-of-a-kind items.

The man-machine team can often be very efficient; e.g., buildings are being designed and built today with as much as one third less steel than would have been required under previous techniques.

COMPUTERS WILL BE USED TO PROCESS LANGUAGE

The difficult subject of language processing presents a dichotomy similar to the one discussed above under image processing. In its simpler form of processing, the language is stored in the computer which can, based on the use of an index to find the correct words, parrot it back. For example, in the system recently installed for the New York Stock Exchange, up-to-the-second information is "spoken" by the computer in response to a code number for a given stock which is dialed into the computer over a private telephone line.

In more sophisticated systems, the computer will, in a sense, know the meaning of the language it has stored and be able to respond to complex inquiries after analyzing the language of the inquiry to determine what was asked for. While the problem is very difficult and progress will be slow, nonetheless, in the next decade many systems will be able to be queried in English, albeit with limited vocabularies and stylized syntactical constructions.

Systems already exist which mecahnically translate some 100,000 words of Russian each day. The quality is not high, but the cost and elapsed time are such that the customer finds it useful. Whether machines will be able to translate within the next decade as well as an expert human translator is doubtful.

INPUT/OUTPUT DEVICES WILL BECOME MORE VARIED, MORE FLEXIBLE, AND LESS EXPENSIVE

As costs of the electronic portions of computers decline substantially, input/output costs will dominate, particularly for computer utilities. Consequently, considerable emphasis will undoubtedly be given to research and development aimed at reducing the costs of existing i/o devices and to inventing new ones.

Some of the existing devices are telephone sets, punched cards and tickets, paper and magnetic tape, keyboards of various kinds, character readers, printers, display devices, microphones and loudspeakers, tablets to write or draw on, measuring instruments which read directly into the computer, and actuators.

Terminals for Computer Utilities. The least expensive and most readily available terminal device for computer utilities is the telephone. If the voice recognition problem could be solved, it would be possible to speak instructions into a computer and have it respond in kind. But it appears that such a very difficult process will become feasible on only a very limited basis during the next decade. However, the dial and, more importantly, the touch-tone system with buttons which is just now becoming available can be used to introduce information into the computer system.

However, the telephone is quite inadequate for many applications. Its ten positions restrict input to numerical information, or information must be coded as a number. No written record of the question or the answer is available. However, simple reading devices (e.g., an embossed plastic card) exist which can be attached to phones, and the development of inexpensive, simple printers that can be attached is a reasonable expectation. In time, the most common terminal device of an information utility will probably be a typewriter or something similar, although the typewriter has the drawback of a rather limited rate of input or output.

In addition to the typewriter, a display such as might be obtained from a television picture tube would be desirable. A display device, which might be in color and have greater resolution than today's television set, would permit a computer to present such pictorial information as a portion of a page from a Sears' catalog or the floor plan for an architect. In effect, one could "browse" through a catalog or file of information.

The more affluent user might want a device for reproducing on paper what was displayed (probably not in color for some years) ; a reader for the input of pictorial information, including printed material; a magnetic tape unit for recording various kinds of information, including video; a tablet to write and draw pictures on; and voice input and output.

With the exception of voice recognition, each of the above is technologically feasible today. Though quite expensive, much of it is economically feasible for such specialized applications as automated design. By 1975 this "Cadillac" of terminals may cost no more than a Cadillac. But even if the cost were much greater, many firms would find such a system economical, and large firms would have many. Even many individuals will be in a position to afford such a system, with the cost justified by an increase in the user's productivity.

Character Recognition. The use of character recognition devices for putting information into computers will expand considerably. Such systems have been in use for a number of years in banking, credit card applications, utility billing, etc., but they have been limited in the sense that they distinguish among only a few different symbols (fourteen in the banking system) printed in a highly stylized font. However, systems are now available for handling character sets with many symbols and in a variety of type faces, and though still quite expensive, they are economically feasible for large-volume jobs. Since they contain much electronics, they can be expected to become less costly.

In the future, in those instances where the data must be typed in order to be fed into a character reader, it will normally be less expensive to bypass the character reader by having the typewriter connected directly to a computer utility. This will permit editing the data and putting it into a format.

Character recognition systems will be used increasingly for reading printed documents such as airplane tickets and "turn around" documents. An example of the latter is a magazine subscription renewal notice mailed to a customer with information printed on it by the computer. The subscriber puts a check with it, and "turns it around" by mail to be read by the machine.

If reading typewritten characters is difficult, reading handwritten characters would seem impossible for computers. However, the problem can be simplified and solved; e.g., we can train the writer to make characters in a special way. Thus we have the equivalent of the highly stylized font used on bank checks. If the machine can capture the information as it is written (which it could if a man were writing on a tablet at a terminal of a computer utility), the problem is easier. Further, if the machine can immediately display back to the writer the output of its recognition process, the writer can check its correctness and try again if necessary. Such systems exist in the laboratory today.

However, there is little likelihood in the next decade that a machine will be able to recognize an undisciplined scrawl. Signature verification and identification of individuals by their handwriting are simpler problems and will be done by computers before the general problem is solved.

Voice Recognition. A subfield of pattern recognition with important implications for the future is voice recognition. To the author's knowledge, no voice recognition system is presently in use on a daily basis. Laboratory work has been going on for some time, and fairly reliable systems exist where a few speakers can use a few simple sounds, such as the ten numeric digits. A voice recognition device capable of recognizing numbers, letters, and a few one-syllable words would have a large market, and may exist at a reasonable price by 1970. Systems capable of handling larger vocabularies (five hundred to a thousand words) will probably exist by 1975. Even the simpler of such systems would be useful for direct inquiries into an information utility via telephone or radio.

The problem of identifying who spoke is apparently somewhat easier than understanding what is said, particularly if the system is asked only to verify that the speaker is who he claims to be (assuming his voice-print already exists in the machine). Should a market develop, such identification systems could probably be available within five years.

Fingerprint Recognition. Systems capable of identifying individuals whose thumbprints are on file may be available within five years. Some experts believe that such systems may be realized within eighteen months. In addition to their obvious applications in law enforcement, these devices may become inexpensive enough for business to make the thumb the universal credit card (which cannot be lost or stolen).

Pattern Recognition. Many other pattern recognition tasks could have considerable impact if done by computers. For example, the ability to recognize meaningful patterns in electrocardiogram and electroencephalogram traces and in photomicrographs of biological cells would improve and reduce the cost of medical care.

THE EXTENT THAT INFORMATION UTILITIES ARE USED WILL DEPEND ON COMMUNICATION COSTS AND CAPABILITIES

The information utility concept and the expending use of computers discussed here are dependent on efficient and low cost communication. Demand for data communication capability will increase tremendously in the next decade. As night be expected, communications and computer experts disagree on whether communications or computer technology will limit the introduction of information utilities which are dependent on both. Communications experts point to large projected investments in new facilities, and they anticipate that data transmission volume will exceed voice transmission prior to 1970. On the other hand, computer experts believe the demand may be even greater than that anticipated by the communications specialists; they also fear that a communications plant designed for an earlier era may not be able to handle appropriately the type of communications required in the era of the information utility. For example, at present, the minimum period of time that can be bought is three minutes; yet a computer utility user might need but a few thousandths of a second at a time. One reason for the large minimum is the slowness of present electromagnetic switches used in telephone central offices.

Beginning in a few years, the telephone industry plans to install electronic switching systems at the rate of about one new electronic office each day; but even at that rate, the replacement will not be complete until around the year 2000. Of course, the change will first be made in the large metropolitan centers where the demand for data transmission will be greatest. Nonetheless, at the projected installation rate, the changeover will not reach 50 per cent completion until after 1980.

Some computer experts believe that because this replacement system has been designed primarily to handle the traditional voice (analog) traffic, it will not provide the best system for handling data (digital) traffic. Therefore, they suggest consideration of other possibilities for handling the digital load; e.g., a new all-digital communication system specifically designed for digital traffic that could easily handle voice traffic as well, and could offer other advantages. While they agree that such an implementation would be costly, they point out that so is the common carrier plant.

It appears to be of utmost importance from the standpoint of the information utilities to create a national communications system which—

(a) is designed for very rapid growth in digital triffic;
(b) is capable of changes in function to keep pace with technology;
(c) provides *secure* user-to-user and computer-to-computer communications;
(d) provides dynamic control of priority; and
(e) allows the user to purchase quite small increments of time with electronic switching speeds.

The question of whether the computer or the communications experts are right (a question of economics as well as technology) is far beyond the scope of this report. However, since the communications industry is government regulated, what happens in this field is very much a function of government policy and not solely the result of the forces of the marketplace. The subject deserves considerable study to ensure that government policy is conducive to the growth of communications facilities appropriate for the era of information utilities.

THE COMPUTER HAS ACCELERATED THE PACE OF TECHNOLOGICAL CHANGE IN THE PAST AND WILL CONTINUE TO DO SO

Although scientific and engineering applications of computers have thus far been virtually ignored in this report, such use still accounts for a large percentage of the total computing power consumed. The growth of technology in some fields, such as nuclear physics and space, has been completely dependent on computers. Other fields have been essentially untouched—but they will not be for long.

In the past, even in fields of science and engineering where computers have been used, their application has been limited by the relative difficulty of operation. It has been estimated that fewer than 20 per cent of the engineers and scientists who should use computers ever do so. However, coupling better higher level languages with an online terminal of a computer utility will have a strong impact on computer use by engineers and scientists, and therefore will increase the pace of technology. Further, the use of graphical information processing will increase the efficiency of designers.

The computer not only permits the scientist to collect and analyze more data, but it is assuming an integral role in the experimental process. In particular, the computer is now used to control laboratory experiments directly, increasing speed and permitting more complex experiments.

In time, the advent of the information utility will make it feasible to develop information retrieval systems for given areas of knowledge which can be interrogated by anyone. Progress will be accelerated when what is already known becomes more accessible. However, really effective systems which approach the capability of an expert who really knows the literature of his field present formidable problems that are not likely to be solved for some time.

The Social Implications of Computers

When things change rapidly, it is convenient to talk in terms of "order of magnitude," meaning a change by a factor of ten. It is commonly observed that a change of an order of magnitude in a technology usually produces fundamentally new effects. For example, man can travel on foot at speeds around four miles per hour, or move by automobile at forty miles per hour, or by jet plane at four hundred miles per hour. Thus, the automobile is one order of magnitude faster than walking and the jet plane two orders faster. These changes have brought about fundamental changes in our way of life.

Computer speed has improved by at least seven orders of magnitude over hand calculations—a ten-millionfold increase. At the same time, the cost of operation has decreased by something more than ten thousand times, or four orders of magnitude. And changes in computer technology are still taking place. Speed increases of one or two orders are now available in the laboratory, and at least another order decrease in cost appears likely when these devices reach the market. It is reasonable to expect that 1975 will compare with the precomputer era by ten to twelve orders of magnitude in speed (or a thousand billion) and by six to eight orders in cost.

Figure 1 represents the amount of computing power available in the country. So far, it has been doubling each year; i.e., it changes by an order of magnitude in a little over three years. Experts disagree about whether it can continue at that rate, but I believe that it will through 1975. (The broken line in Figure 1 is a more conservative curve, representing a 70 per cent rather than a 100 per cent annual increase.)

Thus, significant changes in our way of life should be anticipated in view of the expected changes in speed, cost, size, and amount of available computer power in the nation, and because of the factors discussed earlier, such as the development of information utilities, pictorial processing, language processing, better and varied input/output devices, and improved ease of use.

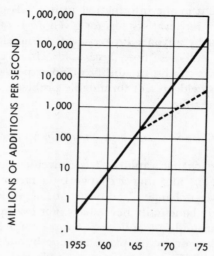

Figure 1. Computing Power in the
United States

Increases in human productivity are to be expected, although the improvement will not be uniform. The over-all impact of computers and technological change should result in an even higher rate of growth in productivity than the economy has enjoyed in recent years. Some types of jobs will disappear, many will change, and new ones will be created. Education, government, industry, unions, and individuals must expect and plan for continuing change, which will become an increasingly important factor in life. Many individuals will have to learn and perform two, three, or more different types of work in their lifetime, and education must be accepted as a continuing, lifelong process. This will be especially true for people in professional and technical occupations. Those who are unable to adapt to change will find life difficult.

In many fields significant changes are taking place well within the period of an individual lifetime. It used to be that a man could go to school, take a job in a profession or in industry, move up in the organization, and do his job well until retirement, drawing on what he was taught in school and on what he learned through experience. In many fields, including business, this is becoming more and more difficult. Without continuing education in new developments, an individual may find himself obsolete. Many companies are even now hiring specialists fresh out of college at the same time that they are terminating older men in the same specialty or restricting the number of older men they will hire. Organizations get into trouble because top management has not kept up with technological change, and individuals are frightened because they know their knowledge and experience are out of date.

EMPLOYMENT

No other social implication of computer utilization receives so much attention as the impact on jobs. When productivity increases faster than demand, people are displaced. When increase in demand matches increase in productivity, no one is displaced, but "silent firings" result as fewer new jobs are generated. More new jobs must be created elsewhere by over-all growth of the economy.

A broad analysis of anticipated increases in productivity is beyond the scope of this report, but needless to say, they will be greatest in activities involving simple processing of information. Let us consider several classes of workers in such activities.

Office Workers. Computers have often been economically justified on the basis of the number of clerks they will replace, yet the percentage of clerical and kindred workers seems to have remained constant over the years. There has been speculation that computers and office automation have retarded growth in white-collar jobs. Yet in 1964 the gain in white-collar employment (3.1 per cent) was greater than the gain for all non-farm employment (2.7 per cent) and the gain for clerical and kindred workers was higher still (3.9 per cent).

On the other hand, the managerial work force has lagged behind all other white-collar subdivisions in rate of growth for some years and declined in 1963; 1964's gain was 2.2 per cent. Since electronic data processing greatly affects the productivity of middle management, it must be assumed that computers have had a role in the declining growth of managers—though to what extent is another matter. This occupational category includes proprietors, and some of the decline may be attributable to the trend toward formation of larger businesses with consequently fewer proprietorships.

Over the next decade, as available computing power continues to grow exponentially, as input/output devices become more elaborate, as computer applications become more sophisticated, as management information systems come into being, and as duplication of effort is eliminated, I believe that middle management, and especially clerical positions, will decline as a percentage of total employment. Increased productivity will have more of an impact on employment in industry than in areas of increasing demand for services (e.g., government and medicine).

Clerical functions of secretaries, stenographers, and typists will be affected in the manner previously discussed, while service aspects of their work will be affected only slightly. With typewriters as terminals on a computer utility, productivity will be increased by reducing retyping to a minimum, and some letters could be composed from paragraphs pre-stored in the computer. Because of difficulties in voice recognition, I do not anticipate the development of a voice-operated typewriter by 1975.

Professional and Technical Personnel. The productivity of professional and technical personnel can be expected to increase significantly in the coming decade because of information utilities and the availability of inexpensive, easier-to-use computer power. Information utilities will make the work of others more readily available. However, in our increasingly technological society, the need for professional, scientific, and technical personnel should continue to grow at a rate faster than the total labor force. This is not to say that professional and technical personnel will not be displaced at times, particularly those involved in increasingly automated design and testing functions. But when displaced, they should be able to find other employment if they have not neglected their continuing education.

Draftsmen. Draftsmen and related occupations should decline after 1970 as the result of the increasing ability of computers to process images and drawings and the introduction of automated design techniques coupled with computer-controlled tools and processes. Even simple systems in existence today can produce detailed construction drawings twenty-five times faster than a draftsman.

Typesetters and Compositors. These occupations are dying out.

Machinists. Numerically controlled (N/C) machine tools can not only turn out work faster than men (from ten to one hundred times as fast), they can produce work to better tolerances and with less spoilage. However, of all machine tools installed today, less than 1 per cent are N/C; and in 1964 N/C sales accounted for about 10 per cent of the total dollar volume. Although there have been dire predictions of gross displacements in the future, it would seem that even by 1975 the majority of machine tools will still be manually operated. Although the total number of machinists may actually decline, this occupation will continue to provide a large number of jobs in the next decade.

Sales Personnel. Large-scale machine vending of goods is not expected to materialize by 1975, although its use will increase. By 1975 some sales will be made from a catalog via an information utility. Nonetheless, the customer's desire to touch and see and ask questions, coupled with the seller's wish to have a salesman to push his goods will require sales personnel. Their productivity will be increased by a reduction of clerical functions (e.g., taking inventory, making out sales slips, etc.). Better inventory control will reduce investment in goods and ensure that what the customer wants is more often in stock. Sales-reporting systems via telephone for salesmen on the road will speed up the ordering process and result in better service to the buyer.

EMPLOYMENT IN THE INFORMATION-PROCESSING FIELD

Although information-processing equipment has displaced workers in some fields, a whole new industry has developed that provides several hundred thousand new jobs. Already a multibillion-dollar industry, sales in the information-processing field have been growing at a rate of 25 to 30 per cent per year, and there seems little doubt that a 15 to 20 per cent growth can be maintained over the next decade.

Statistics exist only on production workers for the manufacturers of computers and related equipment. In 1963 about 100,000 were employed, an increase of 23 per cent over 1958 but a decrease of 1 per cent from 1962. Because of increasing automation, this number will probably continue to decline despite rapidly increasing sales. One manufacturer predicts that by 1967 his direct labor costs will approximate 1 per cent of his sales price.[2]

Sales and service personnel will continue to increase at a rapid rate, as will those involved in analysis, programing, and operation of equipment. The number employed in these occupations today is estimated between 200,000 and 350,000. Analysis—deciding what the computer is to do and designing appropriate procedures—will grow the fastest in the next decade. By 1970 the numbers of people engaged in analysis may be three times what it is today. Next fastest will be programing—writing out the instructions for the computer. This function will be increasingly carried out by the computer itself so that the number of programers will not grow as fast as it has in the past. However, it will likely double by 1970.

On the other hand, the function of computer console operator will almost cease to exist in the computer utility of tomorrow, and consequently their numbers can be expected to increase only through 1970 and then level off.

One of the jobs created by office automation is that of keypunch

[2]Max Palevsky, "Tomorrow's Data Processing and Computers," *Interface 4*, Scientific Data Systems, speech given at Institute of Management Sciences, Los Angeles, California, April 30, 1965.

operator, and the demand has never been higher than it is today. The use of optical character recognition devices, the capturing of data at its source, computer-to-computer communication, plus other factors leading to better productivity, should eventually cause the growth of keypunch job opportunities to level off. Over the next five years, however, continued rapid expansion of computer use should offset jobs lost to mechanization. Thus, while keypunch operators will often be displaced by a machine, they will be able to find jobs elsewhere; whether this will be the situation in the 1970s, however, is a matter of disagreement among the experts.

COMPUTERS AND PRIVACY

As we go through life, we leave behind a trail of records. The first is our birth certificate, followed by medical records and then educational data, including grades, behavior, IQ test scores, and personality profiles. We may spend some time in the military service. We obtain a social security card and start a history of employment records. We get a driver's license. Some of us will receive traffic citations, and others may have police records for more serious offenses. The list is endless.

Today, these records are widely dispersed and generally inaccessible in their totality without a great deal of effort and diligence. The price for putting together a complete personal history of an individual, even with his cooperation, is very high; without his cooperation, it is tremendous. In the future, it is likely that such information will be centralized and easily accessible, at least to some. Unless appropriate precautions are planed now, an unscrupulous individual would be able to turn up scandalous and defamatory information, where it exists, with comparative ease.

Up to the present time, it usually has been possible for an individual to escape his past. But with computerized information services, if one ever runs afoul of the law as an adult, does poorly in school, has a poor credit record, or suffers a heart attack, the records will be comparatively easy to get at. From some viewpoints, this may be socially desirable, but the basic question is the wisdom of having all aspects of a person's past life a completely open book.

If society regards such a lack of privacy as unacceptable, then safeguards must be built into our information systems. We suffered many fires before adequate electrical codes were developed. Let us hope that we can be wiser this time and incorporate adequate safeguards into the information systems now under construction.

The Rate of Development and Diffusion of Technology

by Frank Lynn, INTEC, Incorporated

UNDERSTANDING THE PROCESS OF TECHNOLOGICAL INNOVATION

The traditional "Horatio Alger" of technological innovation is a young man who, while working late one night in a homemade laboratory in his basement, accidentally makes a major new discovery that is quickly adopted by industry. Part of this story, with some variations, has happened in life a number of times in the past (e.g., Bell with the telephone, Morse with the telegraph, and Goodyear with rubber), and probably is happening today, although to a much lesser extent than during the nineteenth and early part of this century. However, the portion dealing with the commercial development and exploitation of a new discovery is largely a myth in our modern industrial society.

Although it is possible for a technological innovation to be discovered by an individual and achieve widespread application by word of mouth or by a technique that does not involve a deliberate investment of capital for commercial development and exploitation, the rate at which it is diffused would be so slow that the ensuing changes would not be a matter of concern. In our modern society, a major technological innovation is characteristically introduced by a company or group of companies which recognize the potential commercial application of a technological innovation (discovered by themselves or others) and invest considerable effort and funds in developing it commercially and exploiting its applications. This type of success story can be found in the history of such innovations as synthetic fibers, radio and television, electronic computers, and frozen foods. It is of particular concern because changes resulting from this type of technological innovation can occur so quickly that natural economic and social forces may not be able to react and adjust effectively, thereby creating problems in our society.

In order to anticipate, identify, and cope with the problems created by technology, it is necessary to know more about the process of technological innovation, the factors that influence the rate at which innovations diffuse into our economy, and the methods by which this diffusion can be measured.

The Measurement of Technological Innovation. Technology is one of the major forces that continually act and interact upon our economy. Some of these forces, particularly social and economic ones, tend to occur slowly and on such a broad scale that they are difficult to control. Technological changes are usually more dynamic because they tend to occur at a much faster rate and are, to some extent, controllable by the amount of funds invested in their exploitation.

A major problem in measuring technological change is the difficulty in distinguishing between the two basic components that together determine the change—the number of technological innovations introduced, and their rate of diffusion.

The rate of development and diffusion of technology is critical because it determines whether sufficient time is available for natural forces within our economy and society to adjust to changes accompanying innovations. If this rate is accelerating so that the adjustment period is too short, then methods for anticipating the impact of technological changes and instituting corrective measures may have to be developed.

THE RATE OF DEVELOPMENT AND DIFFUSION OF TECHNOLOGY

Periodically throughout history, some technological innovations have been developed which have a very significant social and economic impact. They create a major new industry, displace or make obsolescent existing products, provide an important new medium of communication, or even alter the way we live. Such technological innovations as the steam engine, line casting machine, telephone and telegraph, electric light, and internal combustion engine fall into this category, as do such more recent innovations as radio and television, the airplane, synthetic resins, the vacuum tube, the automobile, and synthetic fibers. Some recent technological innovations which appear to meet this criterion include electronic computers, semiconductors and integrated circuits, synthetic leather, numerical control, and atomic power generation.

This is a study of the rate of diffusion and development of twenty technological innovations that have created, or are expected to create, entire new industries, displaced existing products and processes, changed training and skill requirements of workers, or made an important contribution to society. The purpose of the study is to determine insofar as possible from a number of case studies whether the time involved in the development and diffusion process was tending to accelerate over time.

The list appears to include most of the technological innovations that have had a major impact on our economy and society during this century. The selection also provides a reasonable balance between other factors influencing the rate of development and diffusion of technology. However, because of the limited number of innovations involved, these factors are intermixed to such an extent that considerable judgment had to be used in assessing the importance of each.

Measuring the Rate of Development and Diffusion. The yardstick used to measure the rate of development and diffusion for such diverse technological innovations as electronic computers, frozen foods, synthetic fibers, and nuclear power generation was "time." This required the definition of certain critical reference points within the entire process of technological development and diffusion in order that lapsed time could be measured and compared in a reasonably objective manner.

Four steps in the process were identified:

1. *Basic research and investigation.* The period of basic research and investigation can best be defined as the time when knowledge is generated for knowledge's sake. In most instances, the beginning of this period, when the original idea occurs, is impossible to ascertain, for it may be traced as far back as Greek mythology (the airplane) or early science fiction (television). Therefore, no attempt was made to measure this period other than to note some of the more outstanding fundamental research and experimentation that preceded the discovery of each innovation.

2. *Incubation period.* The incubation period begins when technical feasibility of an innovation is established, and ends when its commercial potential becomes evident and efforts are made to convert it into a commercial product or process. The existence of an incubation period is in direct conflict with the widely held concept that a basic technological discovery is immediately followed by a hectic period of development as individuals and companies rush to convert the innovation into a commercial product or process. Although this has happened with several recent innovations (e.g., semiconductors and lasers), this is the exception rather than the rule. For most innovations, a period of time lapses (sometimes quite long) when very little progress is made or even attempted to convert the discovery into a commercial product or process.

There appears to be no single reason for this incubation period; rather, it results from technical, economic, and/or market factors which influence the assessment of the commercial potential of an innovation. For example:

> Radio was originally viewed as an adjunct to the telephone and telegraph as a medium of private communication; its potential role as a medium of mass communication through broadcasting was not recognized until several years after it was in use commercially for private communication purposes.

> The process for manufacturing synthetic rubber was available for more than twenty years before commercial development was started. The commercial potential of the process did not become evident until technical advances had been made in the production of required raw materials.

> Frozen foods had to await the creation of an economic climate in which the consumer was willing to pay a premium for the convenience of these foods.

> The commercial potential of the vacuum tube did not become evident for eight years after its initial discovery, until research on the nature of electron flow in a high vacuum was successful.

The incubation period could be of particular importance to changes in the rate of development and diffusion of technology because the period could be shortened significantly in the future by industry's long-range and product-planning activities.

3. *Commercial development.* Commercial development begins with the establishment or recognition of the commercial potential of a technological innovation. It is normally characterized by a decision to undertake development to resolve the remaining technical and economic obstacles to commerical applications of an innovation. This may be undertaken by a company, the federal government, or even a private individual, but it is always a directed effort to reach a reasonably well defined commercial objective. In addition, this period includes the time and effort required to develop the required production processes and equipment. The commercial development period ends when the innovation is introduced as a commercial product or process.

4. *Commercial growth (diffusion).* The diffusion of technological innovations into consumer and industrial applications is a complex process which determines the rate at which the changes brought about by technology will affect our economy. The commercial growth cycle followed by innovations typically involves an interplay of technical and economic factors—new applications increase production by lowering costs, and thereby enlarging the scope of applications. Eventually, the original innovation is displaced by newer innovations or by economic and social changes.

The method employed to measure the rate of diffusion involved the establishment of a series of economic benchmarks, with the lapsed time required for innovations to attain each benchmark determined and compared. Two different sets of benchmarks were used—one, a relative economic measure, based on per cent of Gross National Product (i.e., 0.02, 0.05, 0.10, 0.15, 0.25, 0.50 per cent, etc.), and the other, an absolute economic measure, based on the dollar value of output (i.e., $50 million, $100 million, $250 million, $500 million, etc.) converted to constant dollars based on the 1957–59 Index of Wholesale Prices.

Of these, the per cent of GNP is probably the more valid method of measuring the rate of diffusion over the entire period under investigation, since one of the primary considerations in this investigation is the effect of technological change on employment opportunities. Thus, the GNP-based measurement more accurately reflects this contribution, since average weekly earnings have grown nearly as rapidly during the period under investigation as Gross National Product. (GNP in 1920 was 16 per cent of 1963 GNP, whereas 1920 average weekly earnings were 26 per cent of those in 1963). Therefore, a technological innovation that attained a level of output of 0.25 per cent in 1925 contributed roughly as many new employment opportunities as another innovation that attained a similar level in 1963. Absolute levels of output are not as reliable a measure of the rate of diffusion throughout the entire period under investigation. However, it is much easier to apply than the GNP-based measurement and could be used as a reasonably good indicator over a limited time span.

The Rate of Development of Technology. As indicated above, two distinct steps occur in the process of technological development after the technical feasibility of an innovation has been established:

1. A period ensues when little or nothing of a concrete nature occurs because, although technical feasibility has been established, a number of missing elements must be supplied before the commercial potential becomes evident.

2. Once the commercial potential has been recognized, a period of commercial development ensues when a directed effort is made to convert the basic technology into a technically and economically feasible product or process.

Table 1 shows the incubation period and commercial development period for each of the technological innovations studied and the date when commercial development work was initiated. As the chart indicates, there is a large variation, particularly in the incubation period. For example, frozen foods had an incubation period of seventy-four years, whereas the incubation period for integrated circuits was only two years. A similar variation exists for the commercial development period, ranging from fourteen years for titanium and synthetic leather to only one year for antibiotics. For these twenty innovations, the average incubation period was nineteen years, and for commercial development, seven years. These averages are not particularly important to this investigation except that they emphasize that the time required for a major technical discovery to be converted into a useful commercial product or process (an average of twenty-six years) is far longer than generally recognized.

To assess changes in the rate of technological development during the last sixty to seventy years, the innovations were grouped into three periods, based on the point in time when commercial development work was started. Periods selected were: Early twentieth century (1890–1919); Post-World War I (1920–44); and Post-World War II (1945–64). Each period encompasses a time of substantial growth in this country's economy. Furthermore, the post-World War I and II periods are some-

Table 1. Rate of Development for Selected Technological Innovations

Technological innovation	Start of commercial development	Lapsed time (years)		
		Incubation period	Commercial development	Total development
Aluminum	1944	15	6	37
Motor vehicle transportation	1948	7	4	27
Air transportation	1948	18	8	14
Synthetic resins	1950	12	3	52
Radio broadcasting	1954	11	9	26
Electronic vacuum tubes	1955	4	6	13
Frozen foods	1958	2	9	83
Vitamins	1929	20	11	24
Synthetic rubber	1933	22	11	31
Television broadcasting	1936	6	12	34
Synthetic fibers	1936	26	3	9
Titanium	1939	11	14	40
Antibiotics	1907	49	1	12
Electronic computers	1913	17	6	21
Semiconductors	1914	7	3	10
Numerical control	1916	74	7	25
Synthetic leather	1926	13	14	26
Nuclear power generation	1886	31	3	14
Freeze-dried foods	1891	23	6	10
Integrated circuits	1903	6	3	5
Average		19	7	26

what similar in that during both, wartime technology was rapidly re-oriented to consumer and industrial applications, resulting in a number of significant innovations. Considering the difficulty of matching individual economic characteristics, the three time periods provide a reasonably accurate basis for comparison.

The results of this analysis are shown in Table 2. As this chart indicates, the over-all lapsed time for technological development has declined during the last sixty to seventy years, from a mean of thirty-seven years in the early twentieth-century period, to twenty-four years during the post-World War I period, to fourteen years during the post-World War II period. Surprisingly, the primary reduction in the over-all period is the result of a decrease in the incubation period rather than in the commercial development period. The incubation period declined from thirty to nine years during the last sixty to seventy years, whereas the commercial development period only declined from seven to five years. The results suggest that the acceleration in the rate of technological development can primarily be attributed to the increasing sophistication and activities of business and industry in identifying potential commercial applications of technology. The decrease in the incubation period can be expected to continue in the future as business and industry devote more of their efforts to product and corporate planning directed at the problem.

The relatively small change in the commercial development period suggests that perhaps engineers and scientists have always been reasonably adept at converting a technological discovery to a commercial product or process once the direction and objective of these efforts were determined. However, as Table 1 indicates, several innovations were converted into commercial products in three years or less, and three of these innovations—semiconductors, nuclear power generation, and integrated circuits—were among the most recent. It is therefore reasonable to expect that the rate of commercial development can be increased to some extent if sufficient funds are allocated. With the continuing increase of expenditures by the federal government and private industry for research and development, the lapsed time for commercial development can be expected to decrease further in the future. However, considering that a certain amount of inertia exists in the area of commercial development, it is unlikely that any dramatic reductions will be made during the next five to ten years.

Other factors that could be expected to influence the rate of technological development are also summarized in Table 2. This analysis suggests some interesting patterns concerning the effects of these factors on the incubation period. For example, innovations with industrial applications have an incubation period approximately twice that of those with consumer applications; and innovations developed with private industry funds also have an incubation period approximately twice that of those funded by the federal government. However, no significant difference was found in the incubation period between innovations developed in existing (secondary) industries and new (primary) industries.

Despite their rather substantial effect on the incubation period, none of these factors were shown by this study to have had a significant influence on the commercial development period. Logic would tend to suggest that the rate of commercial development for innovations sponsored by the federal government would be much faster than for those financed by private industry, and that industrial innovations would have a faster rate of commercial development than consumer innovations. But no such pattern was evident from the analysis. Similarly, very little difference existed between the commercial development periods for primary and secondary type innovations.

The Rate of Diffusion of Technology. As indicated above, the rate of technological diffusion was determined by measuring the lapsed time required to attain levels between two established sets of economic benchmarks: one based on per cent of gross national product, which provides a measure of the relative impact on our total economy, and the other,

Table 2. *Summary of the Influence of Various Factors on the Rate of Technological Development*

Factors influencing the rate of technological development	Mean lapsed time (years)		
	Incubation period	Commercial development	Total development
Different time periods:			
Early 20th century (1890–1919)	30	7	37
Post-World War I (1920–44)	16	8	24
Post-World War II (1945–64)	9	5	14
Type of market application:			
Consumer	13	7	20
Industrial	28	6	34
Source of development funds:			
Private industry	24	7	31
Federal government	12	7	19
Type of innovation:			
Primary	19	6	25
Secondary	18	8	26

Table 3. Rate of Economic Growth for Selected Technological Innovations Measured in Relation to Gross National Product

Technological innovation	Date of commercial introduction	Lapsed time (years) required to reach economic levels								
		0.02 per cent GNP	0.05 per cent GNP	0.10 per cent GNP	0.15 per cent GNP	0.20 per cent GNP	0.25 per cent GNP	0.50 per cent GNP	0.75 per cent GNP	1.0 per cent GNP
Aluminum	1892	14	23	50	62	67	>72			
Motor vehicle transportation	1894	5	7	9	10	11	13	15	17	20
Synthetic resins	1910	<25	29	31	36	37	41	>55		
Air transportation	1911	8	17	25	26	26+	28	29	30	30+
Electronic vacuum tubes	1920	5	8	23	23	>44			>42	
Radio broadcasting	1922	1	2	3	4	6	7	22		
Frozen foods	1925	9	12	15	21	26	27	31	38	40
Vitamins	1937	5	>28							
Synthetic fibers	1939	2	6	13	15	22	25	>25		
Synthetic rubber	1940	2	2+	3	4	>24				
Antibiotics	1940	5	5+	10	>24					
Television broadcasting	1945	2	2+	3+	4−	4	4+	5	19	>19
Titanium	1950	6	>14		>13	14				
Electronic computers	1950	6	8	11	13	14	>14			
Semiconductors	1951	5	7	9						
Numerical control	1955	9	>9							
Nuclear power generation	1957	>7								
Freeze-dried foods	1961	>4								
Integrated circuits	1961	>3								
Synthetic leather	1964	>1								

an absolute measure, based on fixed levels of output. The lapsed time required by each of the twenty innovations under investigation to reach the various relative and absolute economic levels is shown in Tables 3 and 4.

The analysis of the changes in the rate of diffusion of technology during the last sixty to seventy years is similar to that made on changes in the rate of technological development, except that innovations were allocated to the three time periods based on the date of commercial introduction rather than the start of commercial development. The time periods remained the same—1890–1919, 1920–44, and 1945–64.

Table 5, which shows the results of this analysis, provides an interesting insight into changes that have occurred in the rate of diffusion of technology during the last sixty to seventy years. It is evident that the rate of diffusion has definitely accelerated during this period, but that the acceleration has taken two different forms. The first is revealed by comparing the lapsed time to reach each economic level for innovations introduced during the first part of the twentieth century and during the post-World War I period. At each economic benchmark, the rate of diffusion for the more recent innovations was two to three times that of earlier innovations.

The second is revealed by comparing innovations introduced during the post-World War I and post-World War II periods. Although the rate of diffusion was almost identical during the early stages of economic growth (i.e., 0.02 and 0.05 per cent of GNP), the time required for post-World War I technological innovations to reach the higher economic levels was considerably longer than for post-World War II innovations—eighteen years as against nine to reach 0.20 per cent of GNP. There is further evidence that our post-World War II economy is able to ingest technology at a faster rate: post-World War II innovations required only four years to grow from 0.02 per cent to 0.20 per cent of GNP, whereas post-World War I innovations required fourteen years, or, more than three times as long. However, two other considerations must be introduced into any evaluation of these findings:

1. Innovations introduced during the post-World War I period were primarily in consumer applications, which subsequent analysis revealed, tend to have a faster rate of economic growth than the industrial innovations which characterized the post-World War II period.

2. Since post-World War II innovations that reached the higher economic levels were those with the fastest rate of growth, it is quite possible that an analysis such as this undertaken in another ten years would show innovations with slower growth rates reaching the higher economic levels.

Table 4. *Rate of Economic Growth for Selected Technological Innovations Measured by Absolute Levels of Output*

Technological innovation	Date of commercial introduction	Lapsed time (years) required to reach economic levels							
		$50 million	$100 million	$250 million	$500 million	$750 million	$1,000 million	$1,500 million	$2,000 million
Aluminum	1892	23	24	53	63	68	70	>72	
Motor vehicle transportation	1895	8	10	12	15	16	17	20	28
Synthetic resins	1910	26	29	31	36	41	43	49	52
Air transportation	1911	10	11	20	21	22	23	23+	24
Radio broadcasting	1922	2	3	4	7	8	21	>42	
Electronic vacuum tubes	1920	7	8	22	23	35	>44		
Frozen foods	1925	10	12	15	25	26	27	29	31
Vitamins	1937	5	6	>28					
Synthetic fibers	1939	2	3	11	14	19	22	24	>25
Synthetic rubber	1940	2−	2+	3	11	22	>24		
Antibiotics	1940	4	6	10	>24				
Television broadcasting	1945	2	2+	3	3+	4	4+	8	15
Titanium	1950	4	>14						
Electronic computers	1950	5	6	8	11	13	14	>14	
Semiconductors	1951	3	4	7	9	14	>14		
Numerical control	1955	6	10	>10					
Nuclear power generation	1957	6	>7						
Freeze-dried foods	1961	4	>4						
Integrated circuits	1961	3	>3						
Synthetic leather	1964	>1							

Table 5. Summary of the Influence of Various Factors on the Rate of Technological Diffusion

Factors influencing the rate of diffusion of technology	Mean lapsed time (years)			
	0.02 per cent GNP	0.05 per cent GNP	0.10 per cent GNP	0.20 per cent GNP
Different time periods:				
Early 20th century (1890–1919)	9	18	29	35
Post-World War I (1920–44)	4	6	11	18
Post-World War II (1945–64)	5	6	8	9
Type of market application:				
Consumer	4	7	10	16
Industrial	8	15	25	29
Source of development funds:				
Private industry	5	10	15	25
Federal government	6	8	12	20
Type of innovation:				
Primary	6	13	20	27
Secondary	5	6	9	17

Thus, the average length of time required to attain these levels would be increased.

Although it is impossible to ascertain the exact magnitude of the bias these two factors introduce into these findings, they act in opposite directions and perhaps offset each other to some extent.

Despite these mitigating factors, the conclusion that the rate of diffusion of technology has accelerated substantially during the last sixty to seventy years is quite evident. Furthermore, this rate has increased not only in the early stages of commercial growth, but apparently it accelerates as the extent of diffusion increases. The net result is that the lapsed time required for technology to produce widespread effects on our economy and society has decreased significantly during this century—perhaps by a factor of four or more.

Finding shown in Table 5 provide an indication of the role of such factors as the nature of the application, source of development funds, and type of innovation on the rate of diffusion of technology. Of these three, the type of market application appears to be of particular importance, since consumer innovations had a rate of commercial growth approximately twice that of industrial innovations—four years as against eight to reach a level of 0.02 per cent of GNP, and sixteen years as against twenty-nine to reach 0.20 per cent of GNP. Apparently, the market for consumer innovations is so much larger than industrial market applications that their potential economic impact and rate of economic growth is greater.

The analysis of the rate of diffusion between innovations financed by public and private development funds provides an indication of the effects of the federal government's defense and space programs. Only a small variation was indicated between the two groups of innovations during the early stages of economic growth, but at the higher economic levels the rate of growth is greater for innovations whose development was financed by the federal government. For example, it required twenty years for private industry-financed innovations to grow from 0.02 per cent to 0.20 per cent of GNP, whereas federal government financed innovations required only fourteen years to attain the same levels.

Freedom from patent restrictions may be a factor accounting for the faster over-all rate of diffusion of federally supported developments. Innovations financed by private industry often are accompanied by a certain degree of patent protection for the sponsoring individual or company. This patent protection restricts other companies' access to the innovation and provides the patent owner with certain exclusive rights to exploit its commercial application. Thus, commercial exploitation of such innovations would likely involve a single firm. In contrast, most technological innovations developed with federal government funds are free of patent restrictions, and, as a result, commercial exploitation of such an innovation might be undertaken simultaneously by a number of firms. When more companies compete in a new area of technology, total investment is normally higher and the rate of economic growth is also probably greater.

A comparison of innovations introduced into existing industries (secondary innovations) with those that required the creation of an entire new industry (primary innovations) revealed a pattern similar to that found between publicly and privately financed innovations. The time required to attain the lower levels of economic growth was approximately equal—six years for primary innovations to reach a level of 0.02 per cent of GNP as against five years for secondary. However, secondary innovations reached a level of 0.10 per cent of GNP in nine years as compared to twenty years for primary innovations to reach the same level. These data appear to indicate that the over-all rate of economic growth for secondary innovations is approximately twice that of primary innovations.

Thus, the rate of development and diffusion of technology appears to have accelerated substantially since the early part of this century, and even since the post-World War I period. For example, innovations introduced during the early part of the century required an average lapsed time of thirty-six years from the start of commercial development for output to equal 0.10 per cent of the Gross National Product (approximately $625 million at 1964 economic levels). Post-World War I innovations required nineteen years to attain the same economic level, and post-World War II innovations only thirteen years. Furthermore, such factors as the source of development funding, type of application, and industry structure into which the innovation is introduced have been demonstrated to have an important effect on the rate of development and diffusion of technology.

CONCLUSIONS

The Commission's principal interest in the rate of development and diffusion of technology can be summarized by two questions:

1. Is the rate of development and diffusion of technology accelerating as a result of rapidly increasing research and development expenditures by private industry and the federal government?

2. If this rate of development and diffusion is accelerating, are the changes caused by technology occurring at such a rapid pace that natural forces within our economy and society cannot cope with them?

The twenty major innovations examined and analyzed in this study are only a small sample of the hundreds and thousands of technological innovations that have been introduced in our economy in recent years and, therefore, there are acknowledged limitations on the extent to which these conclusions can be generalized to encompass the entire field of technology. Nevertheless, the results of this investigation have provided some answers to these questions. As noted, the rate of development and diffusion for technological innovations introduced during the post-World War II period (1945–64) was twice the rate for those introduced during the post-World War I period (1920–44), and three times the rate for innovations introduced during the early part of the century (1890–1919). Furthermore, the lapsed time between a basic technical discovery and the recognition by business and industry of the commercial potential of such a discovery has also declined, from thirty years for innovations in the early part of this century to nine for those introduced during the post-World War III period. Therefore, it is quite evident that the rate of development and diffusion of technology is increasing, and that there is no logical reason to expect this is not to continue to increase during the next five to ten years.

Furthermore, although the rate of development and diffusion is increasing, the lapsed time from basic technical discovery to the point where significant social and economic problems become evident is still relatively long. For technological innovations introduced during the post-World War II period, an average period of nine years ensued from the basic technical discovery before business, industry, or the federal government recognized the commercial potential of the discovery. An additional five years were required to convert the basic discovery into a commercial product or process, and five more years passed before a level of output equal to 0.02 per cent of GNP was reached. Therefore, an average lapsed time of nineteen years from basic discovery and ten years from start of commercial development was required for a technological innovation to reach an economic level where about six to eight thousand jobs would be directly affected. To reach an economic level where significant social and economic effects would probably become evident (perhaps at a level equal to 0.10 per cent of GNP) an average additional three years was required.

From these data, it is apparent that the present rate of development and diffusion of technology does not require the institution of an "early warning system" to identify potential major technological innovations in their early stages of research and development. Almost without exception, those technological innovations that will have a significant impact on our economy and society during the next five years have already been introduced as commercial products or processes; those that will have a significant impact during the 1970–75 period are already at least in a readily identifiable stage of commercial development.

Productivity, Technology, and Employment in Agriculture

by Walter Butcher, Washington State University

INTRODUCTION

During the past twenty-five years output per man-hour and per unit of input in U.S. agriculture have advanced rapidly in comparison with agriculture's earlier productivity gains and with current rates of productivity advances in the nonfarm portion of the economy. The increases in efficiency have been accompanied by major adjustments in the organization of agricultural production and in the combinations of inputs used. By all odds, the most important adjustment has been a substantial reduction in the total amount of labor used in agriculture. The labor-saving technologies that made this reduction possible have made a major contribution to growth in agricultural efficiency, but the adjustments have led to difficult problems as large numbers of farmers, farm workers, and rural youth have had to make the transfer to other employment.

The purpose of this paper will be to review the major technological changes that have been the basic source of improved productivity in agriculture and discuss the interrelations of technological change, adjustments in agricultural employment, and welfare of farm and rural people. In conclusion, future prospects in agriculture will be discussed and certain guidelines to remedial action suggested.

OUTPUT, INPUTS, AND PRODUCTIVITY IN AGRICULTURE

For several decades prior to 1940 agriculture lagged behind the rest of the U.S. economy in the achievement of higher productivity. (See Figure 1.) From 1890 to 1920 productivity in farming grew by only about one third as much as productivity in the nonfarm portion of the economy. During the next twenty years, from 1920 to 1940, productivity advances in agriculture approximately paralleled those in the rest of the economy. Then, from 1940 on, agriculture increased its productivity per unit of input much more rapidly than did the rest of the economy. By 1957 agriculture was able to overcome the earlier deficit and show a greater total gain in productivity for the entire period 1890–1957 than the nonfarm portion.

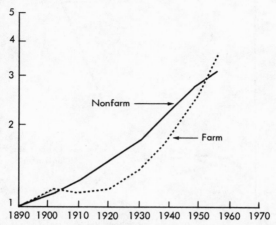

Total factor productivity (output/inputs), farm and nonfarm segments of U.S. economy, 1890–1957; 1890=100.

Year	1890	1900	1910	1920	1930	1940	1950	1957
Nonfarm	100	111	124	145	170	219	271	307
Farm	100	115	114	116	135	173	241	335

SOURCE: Kendrick, *Productivity Trends in the United States*, NBER, 1961.

Figure 1. Total Factor Productivity, Farm and Nonfarm (Ratio Scale)

The productivity trends are more dramatic when considered in terms of output per man-hour. (See Figure 2.) By 1910 the amount of labor used for farm work was already close to its peak, more than twenty years before total input use reached a peak. From 1910 to 1930 the man-hours of labor used in agriculture remained virtually constant at about 23 billion man-hours, and productivity of labor rose slowly with the slight upward trend in total farm output.

During the decade from 1930 to 1940 a slow but unmistakable decline began in the total amount of labor used by agriculture. From 1940 on, the decline in agricultural use of labor was more rapid. Since farm output also grew more rapidly after 1940, the combined effect was a large increase in output per man-hour of approximately 5 per cent per year—more than double the rate of gain in output per unit of input.

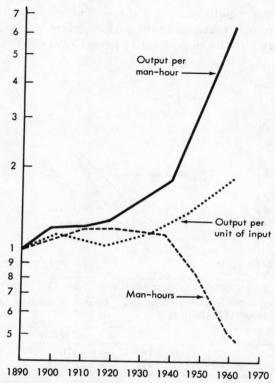

Labor used in agriculture output per man-hour and output per unit of input, 1890–1963; 1890=100.

Year	1890	1900	1910	1920	1930	1940	1950	1960	1963
Output per manhour	100	118	118	125	146	173	291	559	659
Output per unit input	100	112	107	104	111	125	147	178	188
Man-hours	100	110	117	120	116	110	81	51	46

SOURCE: U.S. Department of Agriculture.

Figure 2. Labor Use and Productivity in Agriculture

Improved technology has played the major role in advancing output and efficiency of resource use in agriculture. Output-increasing technological changes have boosted output per producing unit—per acre or per animal—making it possible to meet growing demands without putting more resources into agriculture. The total inputs of labor and capital, taken together, have not increased significantly for several decades. Labor-saving innovations have decreased the labor requirements for farm work and raised the efficiency with which agricultural operations are performed. Both types of innovations contribute to increased ratios of output/inputs and output/man-hour. The output-increasing innovations raise the numerator and the labor-saving innovations make it possible to lower the denominator.

OUTPUT-INCREASING TECHNOLOGY AND OUTPUT LEVELS

A brief summary of major sources of increased farm output is shown in Table 1. During the period from 1919–21 to 1938–40, the reduction in farm-produced power (work animals) accounted for 51 per cent of the total increase in output.

In 1920, 80 million acres of cropland were used just to supply hay and grain to the 27 million draft animals on farms.

Table 1. Percentage Contribution of major Sources of Increase in Farm Output, 1919–21 to 1938–40 and 1940–41 to 1955.

Source of increase	Percentage of total increase	
	1919–21 to 1938–40	1940–41 to 1955
Increased crop production per acre	34	43
Reduction in farm-produced power	51	23
Change in product added by livestock	15	25
Net effect of other sources	0	9
Total	100	100

SOURCE: Donald D. Durost and Glen T. Barton, "Changing Sources of Farm Output," U.S. Department of Agriculture, Production Research Report No. 36, 1960, p. 17.

Increased crop production per acre has been a more durable source of increased farm output and promises to be the major source of future gains. From 1910 to 1930 virtually no increase had been recorded in the U.S. Department of Agriculture's index of crop production per acre nor in the average yields of the major crops. Then from 1930 to 1950 the index of crop production per acre grew by 25 per cent—an average annual increase of 1.1 per cent. From 1950 to 1964 the index grew by 36 per cent—slightly more than 2 per cent per year. In 1964 crop production per acre was approximately two thirds greater than it had been during the period 1910–30. Many of the major crops show even greater increases in yield.

Several technological developments contributed to the increase in crop production per acre. By far the most important of these has been the use of chemical fertilizers.

During the 1940s the amount of commercial fertilizer used more than doubled. This alone accounted for one half of the increase in crop production per acre and 20 per cent of the total increase in farm output. In the 1950s increased fertilizer use contributed two thirds of the increase in crop production and almost one fourth of the increase in total farm output. The use of fertilizer doubled again from 1950 to 1962 and increased by another 20 per cent in just two years from 1962 to 1964.

Other factors which have made important contributions to increased crop production are hybrid seeds, growth of irrigated cropland, pesticides and other agricultural chemicals, better timing of farm operations, and better management throughout the production process.

The product added by livestock has also been contributing an increasing amount to farm output. (Product added by livestock is the amount by which output of livestock exceeds the amount of farm-produced feeds that livestock consume.) Better breeding of animals, more scientific care, scientific mixing of rations, and better control of diseases have all contributed to the rise in product added by livestock. Significantly, the number of breeding units of livestock has increased very little since 1920, but livestock production per breeding unit has doubled.

If the markets for farm products could be easily expanded, an "excess" growth of production capacity would have caused no problems. Unfortunately, the markets for farm products have been unresponsive to market expansion efforts.

The difficulty arises from the fact that more than 75 per cent of agricultural output is used domestically for food, and Americans are, by and large, already well fed and quite disinterested in consuming more food per person. Consumers' incomes are rising, but most additional spending is for products other than food. The small additional amount that is spent for food items goes mostly for more "built-in maid service," and very little additional farm output is sold. Lowered prices, advertising, and other market expansion efforts seem to have little effect on total food consumption. Growth in population is about the only force that consistently works to expand domestic food markets.

The export market has shown considerable growth in recent years, accounting for approximately 20 per cent of the growth in total utilization of farm products from 1950 to 1963. However, the big boost given to exports by growth of foreign assistance during the 1950s may not be duplicated in the near future. Future growth will depend importantly upon growth in purchasing power of countries now existing on a very minimal diet.

Since growth in the market for farm products could not be speeded up to equal growth in output capacity, it has been necessary to reduce the over-all size of the farm productive plant. Output had to correspond fairly closely with markets, either through the operation of supply and demand or through government regulation.

One indication of the extent to which output-increasing technology has led to a reduction in the size of the farm industry is the decrease in acreage of land used for crop production. From 1929 to 1964 the total acres of crops harvested declined from 365 million acres to approximately 300 million.

LABOR-SAVING TECHNOLOGY

Although rising yields have, indirectly, brought about a significant reduction in agricultural labor needs, the largest reduction has come through adoption of labor-saving technologies. The results of substantial progress in labor-saving technology are evident in the decline of man-hour requirements per acre and per animal shown in Table 2. For most major crops, man-hours required per acre of crop dropped to one third or less during the thirty-five-year interval from 1925–29 to 1960–64. Only tobacco production experienced an increase in labor needs per acre due to the effect of rising yields on harvest labor requirements. Data for livestock enterprises, while not strictly comparable, definitely show a downward trend in man-hours per animal. In total, a reduction in labor needs during the period 1929 to 1964 of 11 billion man-hours is accounted for by reduced labor requirements per acre and per animal.

From 1920 on, the number of tractors on farms increased while the numbers of horses and mules decreased. The progress of these changes is shown in Table 3. By 1960 the change-over to tractors was virtually complete, and the 3.1 million horses and mules left on farms performed little if any farm work.

Since the coming of the tractor, mechanization in agriculture has continued to eliminate hand-labor tasks. Corn and cotton pickers have mechanized the harvest of these crops on most farms. Hay harvesting has been more completely mechanized. Machines and chemicals have substituted for much of the hand labor in weed control. Recently, some truly ingenious fruit and vegetable harvesters have begun to replace the large amounts of hand labor used on those crops.

Table 2. *Labor Requirements per Unit for Selected Enterprises, 1925–29 1945–49, and 1960–64*

Enterprise	Unit	Man-hours required		
		1920–29	1940–49	1960–64
Corn for grain ....Acre		30.3	19.2	6.8
Wheat ....do		10.5	5.7	2.9
Tobacco ....do		370.0	460.0	493.0
Cotton ....do		96.0	83.0	47.0
Vegetables, all ....do			[1]119.0	[2]90.0
Hay ....do		12.0	8.4	5.4
Potatoes ....do		73.1	68.5	48.1
Milk cows .... Cow		145.0	129.0	96.0
Cattle and calves ...... Hundred weight ....of beef		4.3	4.0	2.9
Broilers ....100 birds		32.0	15.6	3.3

[1]As of 1939.   [2]As of 1959.

SOURCE: Robert C. McElroy, Reuben W. Hecht, and Earle E. Gavett, "Labor Used to Produce Field Crops," U.S. Department of Agriculture, Statistical Bulletin No. 346, 1964.

Reuben W. Hecht, "Labor Used to Produce Livestock," U.S. Department of Agriculture, Statistical Bulletin No. 336, 1963.

Table 3 shows the value of machinery and equipment on farms is now almost seven times as great as in 1940. The total inputs from machinery and mechanical power have increased by two and one half times after correction is made for changes in the level of prices.

Mechanization in agriculture occurred primarily because of the economic gains it brought. In the first place, it has been possible, by using machinery, to perform farm work with less total input of labor, power, and machinery. From 1940 to 1964 the total amount of these three inputs, plus an allowance for power from horses, declined by 40 per cent. During the same time, the percentage of mechanical power and machinery in the total increased from 14 per cent to 48 per cent. A small part of the decline, not more than 8 out of the 40 per cent, may be due to the decline in crop acreages discussed above. The remainder of the reduction in inputs can be attributed to increased efficiency of performing work with relatively large amounts of machinery rather than with large amounts of labor and animal power.

A second incentive to mechanization has been provided by a definite increase in the cost of labor relative to the costs of other inputs. In Figure 3 farm wage rates are compared with the index of machinery prices and costs of motor supplies and fertilizer. The index of wage

Table 3. Progress of Mechanization on Farms: Numbers of Horses and Mules, Tractors, and Major Harvesting Machines; Value of Machinery and Equipment; and Index of Mechanical Power and Machinery Inputs; Selected Years 1910–64

Year	Horses and mules	Tractors	Harvesting machines[1]	Value of machinery and equipment	Index of mechanical power and machinery
	[In millions]				[1957–59 =100]
1910	24.2	2	2	3	20
1920	25.7	0.2	2	3	32
1930	19.1	.9	0.2	3	40
1940	14.5	1.6	.4	$3,060	42
1950	7.8	3.4	1.4	11,314	86
1960	3.1	4.7	2.8	18,613	100
1964	3	4.7	3.0	20,082	101

[1]Grain combines, cornpickers and picker-shellers, pickup balers, and field forage harvesters.
[2]Less than 0.1 million.
[3]Strictly comparable data not available.

SOURCES: *Changes in Farm Production and Efficiency*, U.S. Department of Agriculture, Statistical Bulletin 233, 1965. *Balance Sheet of Agriculture*, 1964.

rates is currently more than 675 per cent of the 1910–14 level, whereas machinery prices have only risen to 405 per cent and motor supplies to 175 per cent of their 1910–13 levels. Farm operators, attempting to keep costs per unit of output low, have obviously found it increasingly profitable to substitute relatively cheap machinery for relatively expensive labor.

FARM EMPLOYMENT AND RURAL POPULATION

A decline in farm employment followed inevitably from the reductions in labor needed for farm work. The exodus of workers from agriculture has, by any measure, been of large magnitude. When the decline began, around 1920, there were 11.5 million persons employed in agriculture. By 1940 agricultural employment had declined to 9.5 million persons. In 1964 it was only 4.7 million persons—about 40 per cent of the 1920 employment.

Agriculture was employing 22 million fewer workers in 1958 than would have been the case if it had held its 1900 share of the work force. The 22 million workers "released" from agriculture made up three fourths of the work force added by expanding industries such as the trades and services. All other industries whose employment grew less

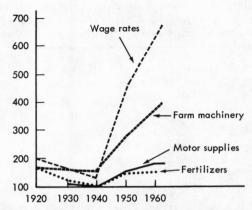

Prices paid by farmers for items used in production 1920–63; 1910–14=100.

Year	1920	1930	1940	1950	1960	1963
Farm wage rates	199	165	140	448	622	675
Farm machinery	163	152	154	282	381	405
Motor supplies		114	102	150	175	175
Fertilizers	167	123	99	149	153	152

SOURCE: *Agricultural Statistics,* 1964.

Figure 3. Trends in Prices of Agricultural Inputs

rapidly than the rate of growth in total U.S. employment released a total of only 7.5 million workers—one third as many as agriculture alone. Thus, to an important extent, declining farm employment has provided the labor force for "growth industries."

Although the movement of workers out of agriculture has been rapid, it has not been rapid enough to bring the agricultural labor force into balance with labor needs under evolving technologies. The primary evidence of imbalance is a persistently low level of agricultural labor earnings as compared with earnings in the rest of the economy. Strand and Heady[1] calculated a labor income per worker on commercial farms of $1208 in 1949—production workers in manufacturing industries averaged approximately $3000 per year at that time. In a more recent study, Johnson[2] concluded that "per capita farm incomes would have to

[1]Edwin G. Strand and Earl O. Heady, "Productivity of Resources Used on Commercial Farms," USDA Technical Bulletin No. 1128, 1955.

[2]D. Gale Johnson, "Labor Mobility and Agricultural Adjustment," *Agricultural Adjustment Problems in a Growing Economy,* (Ames, Iowa: Iowa State University Press, 1958), pp. 163–72.

increase about 50.4 per cent from the 1956 level if comparable labor is to receive the same returns in the farm and nonfarm sectors." Still more recently, Tweeten's[3] estimates for 1959 show average labor incomes of farm operators of $3000 per year, approximately two thirds as much as factory workers' earnings.

The incomes of hired farm workers have also been low in comparison to wages in nonfarm jobs. In 1963 hired farm workers averaged only $6.35 per day of work and only 107 days of work per year. Only nonmigratory workers in the West averaged much above this amount. Farm workers in the South received less than the national average. Significantly, farm workers who had some nonfarm work had average daily earnings at their nonfarm job that were 50 per cent above their earnings at farm work.

The organization of firms and employment in agriculture is conducive to the development of low labor returns during a period of declining labor needs. Only about 7 per cent of all agricultural workers are regular hired employees. The largest number, about two thirds, are self-employed individuals and members of their families. The rest, about one fourth, are more or less casual employees who work only part time or in a succession of temporary short-term positions. Thus, most of the agricultural labor force is not subject to being dismissed by an employer as a direct result of a reduction in the amount of labor needed for farm work. The farm worker, being his own boss, is free to stay on in agriculture as long as he cares to, regardless of whether there is an over-all surplus of farm workers or not. In fact, it is likely that farmers and farm workers will stay in agriculture during a period of declining labor needs *until* there is a substantial labor surplus, because only then will their earnings fall and a change begin to appear attractive. Thus, to some extent, low incomes to farmers and farm laborers must precede any reduction in farm employment. As a result, all farm workers, both those who are needed and those who are not needed, receive low incomes during a downward adjustment in the farm labor force. If employment was organized more along the lines common to other industries, it would be possible to reduce employment without decreasing the incomes of all workers.

Some farmers and farm workers have stayed on in agriculture even though their earnings are now at a disastrously low level. In 1962, 22 per cent of farm operator families had net incomes of less than $2000. In 1964 more than 1.5 million farms, 44 per cent of the total number, had gross sales of less than $2500. Fortunately, the operators of many of

[3]Luther G. Tweeten, "The Income Structure of Farms by Economic Class," *Journal of Farm Economics*, XLVII, 2 (May 1965), 207–21.

these inadequate or nominal farms had off-farm or retirement income to supplement their meager farm earnings. Still, estimates based on 1959 census data show that approximately 6 million rural farm people and 10 million rural nonfarm people had incomes below $3000—the level accepted as an indication of poverty.

In reality, farmers and farm workers having very low incomes are economically unemployed or underemployed regardless of whether they are physically at work for most of the year or not. The total number of rural farm residents that were economically unemployed was calculated to be 1,477,000 persons in 1959—more than 37 per cent of the total rural farm labor force at that time. The percentage of unemployment or its equivalent changed but little from 1949 to 1959, although the absolute number decreased due to a decrease in the size of the farm work force.

Unemployed and underemployed farmers and farm workers are found in many cases to be handicapped, illiterate, or aged, all of which limits their capacity for work. Almost without exception, the farmers with very low incomes have only a meager supply of land and capital to combine with their labor. As a result, they revert to working only part of the time or use antiquated, labor-intensive methods that give correspondingly low returns.

The adjustments now taking place in agriculture are working to correct the labor surpluses and low income problems. From 1939 to 1959 the number of farms with less than $2500 gross sales declined by one half. Most of the decline occurred in the group of farms having no appreciable nonfarm income and a farm business so small that labor earnings averaged less than $500 in 1960. The number of farms in this category declined from 2.2 million in 1939 to 0.2 million in 1964, removing some of the most serious cases of poverty and underemployment in agriculture.

In the past six years a definite downtrend has been registered in the number of farms having gross sales of more than $2500 but less than $10,000. The total number of farms in this category had dropped only 20 per cent in twenty years from 1,686,000 in 1939 to 1,347,000 in 1959. From 1959 to 1964 they decreased to 940,000. Many of the farms in this group are beyond the poverty level on the basis of total income from realized net farm income, off-farm income, and nonmoney income; however, labor earnings per worker are still low, indicating a need for recombination and increases in size.

MOBILITY OF FARM WORKERS

If reductions in the farm labor force had occurred at an even more rapid pace, some of the worst income problems might have been averted.

However, there are limits to the numbers of people that can be trans-
ferred in a short period of time and in a somewhat orderly fashion from
one industry, occupation, or location to another. Unfortunately, several
factors in the agricultural situation reduce the possibilities for rapid
transfer of workers to other jobs.

One hindrance to movement from agricultural to nonagricultural
employment is the relative isolation of agriculture and scarcity of other
industries in many rural farming areas. Thus, a change to nonfarm
employment often requires a change of residence as well as occupation.
The farmer or farm worker faced with this prospect may feel, with some
justification, that he will be at a disadvantage in competing with city
residents for a new job in strange surroundings. Also, a job change that
requires that home ties be broken will be made less quickly than would
a change in the same locality.

One of the ironies of the labor adjustment has been the frequent decline of local nonfarm employment opportunities along with the decline
in need for farm labor. As the number of farms and the farm population
have decreased, so has the business of local trades and services. Thus, the
one possibility in many communities for local nonfarm employment has
often become, instead, a net supplier of labor.

Another hindrance is the lack of transferability of farm skills to nonfarm jobs. A farmer tends to develop skills in a broad range of tasks
ranging from hand labor through machine operation and maintenance
up to management. However, few, if any, of the skills are exactly those
needed by nonfarm employers, nor are they as highly developed as the
skills of an industrial employee with concentrated training and experience. Thus, the farmer or farm worker seeking nonagricultural employment is apt to find that only a small part of his experience and acquired
skill is directly transferable. As a result, many farm-to-nonfarm migrants
find employment in the unskilled occupations where earnings, job security, and job satisfaction are likely to be low.

Lack of education has also hindered many transfers from farm employment. Farmers and farm workers have typically completed fewer
years of school than their industrial counterparts in any occupation
except laborers. And education in rural areas is still running somewhat
below the standards for the rest of the economy.

The group least affected by these hindrances to mobility are the farm
youth. Young people just entering the labor force tend to have fewer
ties to the local community, fewer educational inadequacies, and more
adaptability to developing skills needed in industry. They have moved in
large numbers to seek nonfarm jobs in urban areas.

In 1950 nearly 60 per cent of the farm-nonfarm migrants were under 25 years of age. Thirty-three per cent of the farm-nonfarm migrants were between 14 and 24 years of age, the period when young people are entering the labor force and making early adjustments prior to settling down in a permanent job.

These young people and others migrating from farm to nonfarm areas have tended to show a disappointingly large concentration in the lower-income, semiskilled, and unskilled positions. Several studies have indicated a tendency for farm migrants to concentrate in the categories of laborers, operatives, and craftsmen and foremen in higher percentages than urban migrants or urban residents who did not migrate.

The high rates of out-migration by young people from farming areas are reflected in very low rates of entry of young people into farming. Farm youths who reached 15–24 years of age in 1950 are entering farming in about one third the numbers of the counterpart group that reached ages of 15–24 in 1910. By 1960 the exodus was even more apparent— there were only sixty-two thousand farm operators between 15 and 24 years of age. This is only about one seventh the number of young farm operators entering in 1910 and only slightly over one third of the 1950 number. The total number of young farm operators under 35 years of age in 1960 was only 464,000. In 1950 there had been nearly twice as many young farmers and in 1910, almost four times as many. Clawson concludes, "Men do not withdraw from farming even under considerable provocation; they simply refuse to enter it when prospects are not good. This is further evidence that the salvage value is low for the farmer whose education, experience, and dedication are to agriculture. Having made his choice and having spent a major part of his adult life as a farmer, he is reluctant or unable to leave even in the face of low returns. On the other hand, not yet having chosen or begun a life occupation with the prospect of hard work and low income staring him in the face, he [the young person who might have become a farmer] leaves the farm for employment elsewhere."[4]

The present age distribution of farmers favors a continued reduction in numbers of farmers by holding entries low and letting natural exits through death and retirement bring about the adjustment in numbers. In 1959 there were 1.4 million farmers 55 years of age or older, not significantly lower than the 1.6 million farmers who were 55 or over in 1949. On the basis of past experience, we can expect a decline of nearly 1 million from this group during the 1960s. And in 1970 there will still

[4]Marion Clawson, "Aging Farmers and Agricultural Policy," *Journal of Farm Economics* (February 1963), pp. 13–30.

be almost as many farmers reaching these ages of heaviest exit. Thus, for some time to come, the potential for decreases in the number of farmers will continue at almost the same absolute level as in the recent past. The extent to which this decrease in farm numbers will be realized depends upon two factors—the extent to which further adjustments in farm numbers are needed, and the existence of nonfarm job opportunities for rural youth and young adults.

An approach to estimating the potential for reducing farm employment is to calculate the output per man on efficiently organized farms and determine the number of workers needed on that basis to produce current farm output. Morris and Kadlec[5] estimated that output per full-time man in agriculture was more than twice the present output per average worker. On "superior Midwestern farms," output per worker was three times as great as that calculated output per full-time man. Thus, it is conceivable that eliminating partial unemployment among farm workers and achieving presently attainable levels of productivity would make it possible to supply our present markets while using only one sixth as much labor. An increase of that magnitude in output per man would imply a reduction in farm employment from the current level of 6.1 million down to approximately 1 million full-time farm workers.

With indications of need for further reductions in farm labor force, attention is turned to the possibilities of attracting the more mobile farm workers to nonfarm employment. Evidence from past experience clearly indicates that the most essential element to continuous flow of labor from agriculture is a high rate of employment in the nonfarm economy. The Great Depression of the 1930s stands out as a clear example of a period in which high unemployment in the nonfarm economy stopped migration from farms. During 1930–35 annual net migration from farms was only fifty-eight thousand, less than one tenth as great as during any other period from 1920 to 1964. Another indication of the effect of unemployment is given by Bishop's[6] finding that the rate of migration from agriculture tended to increase by about 0.6 per cent for each 1 per cent decrease in the rate of unemployment in the nonfarm economy. Workers, whether they be farm or nonfarm, are reluctant to leave their present position, poor though it may be, to take a chance in a job market where unemployment is high.

[5] W. H. M. Morris and John E. Kadlec, "An Evaluation and Projection of Output per Man in Agriculture," *Journal of Farm Economics* (December 1963), pp. 1007–11.
[6] C. E. Bishop, "Economic Aspects of Changes in Farm Labor Force," in *Labor Mobility and Population in Agriculture*, Ames, Iowa, Iowa State University Press, 1961, pp. 36–49.

The Leisure Component of Economic Growth

by Juanita M. Kreps and Joseph J. Spengler, Duke University

GROWTH AND DIMENSIONS OF LEISURE

Today's worker receives the equivalent of a four-month holiday, paid each year. If he followed his grandfather's schedule of hours per week he could work from October through May, then vacation till October. Or if he preferred, he could work April through November, and ski all winter.

He takes his nonworking time in different forms, but in total he enjoys about 1200 hours per year more free time than did the worker of 1890. Moreover, he enjoys more years in which he doesn't work at all; he enters the labor force much later in life, and has several more years in retirement than his grandfather. In total, this increase at the beginning and the end of work life has given him about nine additional nonworking years. Yet, lest the worker of today be labeled a loafer, it should be noted that since he lives longer, he works more hours in his lifetime than his predecessor; if born in 1960 he will probably log about 6800 more hours than the male born in 1900.

The Forms of Leisure. On the average, the employed person worked 40.7 hours a week in 1963; in 1890 the average was 61.9. Paid holidays have increased by at least four per year during this period, to about six at present, and paid vacations averaging one and one half weeks per year have added at least six days free time annually. Sick leave amounts to the equivalent of one week, giving the following increases in nonworking hours per year between 1890 and the present:

Source	*Approximate hours*
Reduction in workweek (21.2 per week)	1100
Increase in paid holidays (4 days)	32
Increase in paid vacations (6 days)	48
Increase in paid sick leave (1 week)	40
Total increase	1220

Thus, the shortened workweek has accounted for most of the century's rise in free time during work life. The addition of nine years of non-working time raises the male's number of years outside the labor force by about 50 per cent. If, instead of spending this free time in gaining additional education and in retirement, a man worked on the average two thousand hours per year during these years, he would work during his lifetime an additional eighteen thousand hours, or 435 hours per year (with a work-life expectancy of 41.4 years). Thus the amount of non-working time bunched at the beginning and end of work life has grown by about one third the amount added annually through workweek reductions, added vacations, etc.

Labor Force Size and Composition. During the same period, however, increasing numbers of women have taken jobs outside their homes; the proportion of the adult population in the labor force has therefore remained relatively stable. Despite the fact that the changing sex composition of the labor force would appear to be shifting from men to women, the effect of better household appliances, smaller families, and the sharing of household tasks is to apportion the increased leisure to both sexes.

Potential Growth in Leisure. The increase in nonworking time that has characterized the American economy during the twentieth century has in some degree reflected preferences for leisure as compared with income. In broad terms, the summary statement that about two thirds of the century's productivity gains have been taken in the form of goods and one third in free time suffices, although this statement alone obscures important issues such as the forms leisure has taken (and the extent to which these forms were in accord with workers' preferences), the distribution of nonworking time among the population, and the offsets against this freed time; e.g., longer commuting time to work. If, however, society has taken roughly a third of its increase in output potential in the form of leisure, the alternative statements that present leisure (as compared with that available in 1890) is "worth" approximately $314 billion, or that GNP which includes the value of leisure as well as the value of goods and services is about $941 billion (instead of $627 billion), provide crude estimates of the dollar value of our growth in leisure. If account is taken not only of the increase in material goods and services but also of the amount of leisure created, per capita growth in the economic value of output has not slowed down significantly.

Of more importance for present purposes, perhaps, is the question of the possible growth of leisure in the future. Long-range projections of the growth in nonworking time in total have not been made, perhaps because of the difficulties inherent in anticipating man's future elasticity of demand for goods in terms of effort. Despite great public interest in particular issues—shortened workweek, early retirement, etc.—which will determine the pattern into which leisure will fall, the potential magnitude of our leisure component has received little explicit attention.

The dimensions of future leisure can be indicated under varying assumptions as to growth in productivity and preferences as between goods and leisure. In Table 1 the basic assumptions are: Between 1963 and 1985 the growth rate will be 4.1 to 4.2 per cent per year, population will grow by 1.5 per cent annually, and unemployment will average 4.5 per cent. Assuming no change in working time, the GNP at projected rates of growth would approximate $1544.5 billion in 1985, about two and one third times its present level in 1960 dollars. Per capita GNP would rise from $3181 to $5802, or more than 80 per cent, despite the increased population size.

These increases in total and per capita GNP are possible, then, if working time of roughly forty hours per week for an average of forty-nine weeks per year is continued. At the other extreme, if one supposes that all growth, except that amount necessary to hold per capita GNP constant at $3181, is taken in leisure time, the possible increases in free time are indicated in the remaining columns. The workweek could fall to twenty-two hours by 1985; or it would be necessary to work only twenty-seven weeks of the year; or retirement age could be lowered to thirty-eight years. If the choice were made to divert the new leisure into retraining, almost half the labor force could be kept in training; if formal education were preferred, the amount of time available for this purpose might well exceed the normal capacity to absorb education.

It is, of course, not likely that the work week will drop to twenty-two hours or that retirement age will decline to thirty-eight years. Nor is it probable that during the next two decades workers will continue on their present schedules, thereby taking all productivity gains in the form of a greater quantity of goods and services. If, instead, two thirds of the output growth accrues as goods and services and one third as leisure, GNP would rise to more than a trillion dollars by 1980, and to $1.3 trillion by 1985. Per capita GNP would increase to more than $4400 by 1980 and to approximately $5000 in 1985. (See Figure 1.)

The leisure which accounts for the remaining one third of the growth potential could be distributed in any one way or a combination of several ways; different priorities would be assigned by different persons. If

Table 1. Prospective Growth in Productivity and Possible Uses of Released Time

Year	Possible increases in real GNP (1960 dollars)		Alternative uses of potential nonworking time				Education and training	
	GNP (billions)	Per capita GNP	Total number of years	Retirement age	Length of workweek (hours)	Vacation time (weeks)	Labor force retrained1 (per cent)	Years of extended education
1965	$ 627.3	$3181	....	65 or over	40	3	......	......
1966	655.6	3280	2,245,542	65	39	4	2.9	1.2
1967	685.6	3382	4,655,526	63	38	7	5.0	2.4
1968	707.1	3490	6,910,648	61	36	7	8.7	3.4
1969	745.3	3578	8,880,092	59	36	8	11.1	4.2
1970	779.3	3690	11,263,301	57	34	10	13.8	5.1
1975	973.4	4307	23,135,642	50	30	16	26.2	9.4
1980	1250.2	5059	35,586,729	44	25	21	37.2	13.8
1985	1544.5	5802	47,200,158	38	22	25	45.2	17.5

1Figures are in addition to the number of workers now trained in public and private programs.
SOURCE: GNP projections and employment data from National Planning Association, Report No. 65–1, March 1965. Labor force data for other computations taken from *Manpower Report of the President*, March 1965, p. 248, Table E–2.

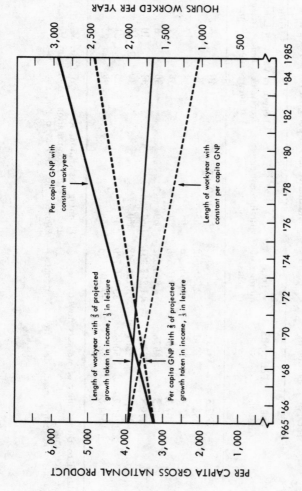

SOURCE: GNP projections and employment data from National Planning Association, Report No. 65-1, March 1965. Labor force data for other computations taken from *Manpower Report of the President*, March 1965 p. 248, Table E-2.

Figure 1. Alternative Uses of Economic Growth Per Capita Gross National Product and Hours Worked, 1965-85

it is conceded that present unemployment is due in some significant degree to qualitative deficiencies in the labor force, however, the first priority might be assigned to job retraining. Hence, a policy decision could be made to retrain a minimum of 1 per cent of the labor force annually, taking the necessary time from that freed or released by the growth in productivity. A second order of preference might be an increase in vacation time, at least until an average of one additional week accrues to the worker. By 1968 these two goals—retraining 1 per cent of the labor force and increasing vacation time by one full week—could be attained. If after these achievements, some leisure gains are taken in the form of reductions in the workweek, working time per week could start by declining about one half hour in 1969, the decline increasing to two and one half hours by 1980. (See Table 2.)

Alternative allocations of leisure in the period 1980–85 might be as follows: Given a $4413 per capita GNP in 1980, achieved with a 37.5-hour workweek, a forty-eight-week work year, and providing retraining for 1 per cent of the labor force, society could choose to retrain much more heavily (4.25 per cent of the labor force per year) or, alternatively, could add one and one half weeks per year in vacation. In 1985, when per capita GNP should reach about $5000, the choice could be between retraining almost 7 per cent of the labor force annually or taking an additional three weeks of vacation. Obviously, other choices could be made, involving a further reduction in the workweek, a lowering of retirement age, or an increased educational span for those entering the labor force.

The relevant considerations are at least threefold: One, the total amount of free time made available by the anticipated improvements in output per man hour is extremely great, even when allowance is made for quite rapid rises in real GNP or even in per capita real GNP. Two, the allocation of this leisure is in itself quite important, given the different degrees of utility man may associate with different forms of leisure. Three, the distribution of leisure, being quite unevenly spread over the entire population, requires further consideration. For although the unequal distribution of income among persons has received great attention, it might well be true that that portion of economic growth accruing to man in the form of leisure has in fact been apportioned much less evenly than income. Questions relating to the total volume, the forms, and the distribution of leisure are of some significance in estimating future potentials for growth in output, and particularly in determining the composition of that output.

Table 2. Possible Allocation of Goods and Leisure

	(1) GNP (billions)	(2) Productivity gains (billions)	(3) Value of goods (⅔ of col. 2)	(4) Value of leisure (⅓ of col. 2)	(5) Per capita GNP	(6) Labor force retrained annually (per cent)	(7) Additional vacation (weeks)	(8) Reduction in the workweek (hours)	(9) Hours released for nonworking time (millions)
1966	$ 649.0	$ 19.7	$ 13.1	$ 6.6	$3247	1	....	....	1,507
1967	670.8	40.8	27.2	13.6	3315	1	½	....	3,016
1968	696.3	62.4	41.6	20.8	3388	1	1	....	4,483
1969	713.7	82.7	51.1	31.6	3426	1	1	½	6,667
1970	743.5	107.0	71.3	35.7	3519	1	1	⅔	7,336
1975	888.9	254.5	170.0	84.5	3933	1	1	2⅓	15,036
1980 (a)	1095.0	464.2	309.0	155.2	4413	4.25	1	2½	23,303
1980 (b)	1095.0	464.2	309.0	155.2	4413	1	2½	2½	23,303
1985 (a)	1321.8	697.7	465.0	232.7	4928	6.9	1	2½	30,862
1985 (b)	1321.8	697.7	465.0	232.7	4928	1	4	2½	30,862

SOURCE: See Table 1.

Hours of Work Issues

by Myron L. Joseph, Carnegie Institute of Technology

INTRODUCTION

There are two quite different issues involved in an examination of the "hours of work" question. One is simply whether the long-run reduction in the workweek will continue into the future. The answer is related to the relative value placed on leisure and income by American workers; to the changing industrial, occupational, and labor force structures; and to the implications of workweek reduction for productivity, costs, and growth. The second issue is whether it would be desirable to use the power of government to reduce the workweek, either through an increase in the overtime penalty rate and/or through a reduction in the standard workweek. Although this question could be related to the social desirability of increased leisure, workweek reduction has been considered primarily as a means of increasing employment by spreading available work. These proposals must be evaluated in terms of their employment-creating potential and their costs relative to other policy alternatives.

The historical data show a relatively steady but gradual decline in hours of work from 1850 through 1900. There is no evidence of any dramatic impact of either the ten-hour or eight-hour movements, and it appears likely that the underlying economic forces, including the increasing reluctance of workers to work excessive hours, were at least as influential as political activity or direct union action. (See Figure 1.)

In the first two decades of the twentieth century, working hours were reduced through a combination of collective bargaining, federal legislation, administrative acts, social pressure, and a changing environment in which the eight-hour day became the standard schedule in a growing sector of the economy. In the Depression, Congress passed the Walsh-Healey Act (1936), which established a forty-hour standard for government contract work, and the Fair Labor Standards Act of 1938, which defined a standard workweek for covered establishments and required a time-and-one-half penalty rate for overtime hours. The standard (straight-time) workweek was reduced in stages from forty-four hours in

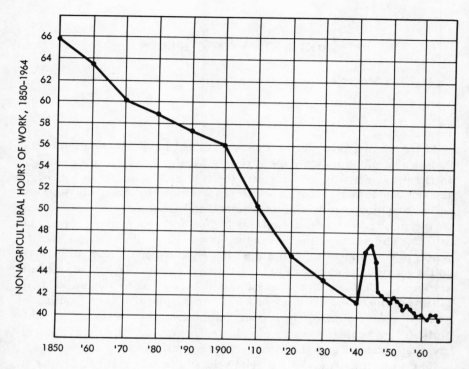

by members of the labor force who were at work. Data are for the month of May
of each year and reflect hours worked at all jobs during the week. These figures are
based on interviews obtained in the monthly survey of households.
SOURCE: 1850–1940; Dewhurst & Associates, *America's Needs and Resources*, 1955.
1943–63; U.S. Bureau of the Census and U.S. Bureau of Labor Statistics.

Figure 1. Nonagricultural Hours of Work, 1850-1964

1938 to forty hours in 1940. As I will suggest later, it is very difficult to
assess the impact of this legislation on the workweek.

As the economy moved into war production from the trough of 1938,
the workweek rose even more rapidly than it had fallen in the Depression. When the war ended, the manufacturing workweek fell from the
45.2 hours war peak to 40.3 hours in 1946. Since then the workweek has
been relatively stable.

THE LESSONS OF HISTORY

It is difficult to identify the lessons to be learned from the historical record. Although the mass movements and political activities associated with the shorter-hours movement before 1900 did not produce dramatic short-run effects, they may have created an environment and expectations that facilitated the sharp reduction in hours during World War I. Collective bargaining cannot be given major credit for the reduction in the workweek prior to 1930, since unions represented only a small minority of the labor force. However, some unions, notably in the building trades, were able to use their bargaining power to reduce working hours substantially, and in doing so undoubtedly helped to set the pattern for the rest of the economy. Although the early legislation was ineffective, the sharpest reduction in the workweek was accomplished with the help of the government during World War I, and the rapid reduction of the workweek after World War II might be attributed to the Fair Labor Standards Act and the collective bargaining agreements that followed the pattern established by that law. But the legislative and institutional record may simply be the transmission belt through which the labor force has reduced the average hours supplied as the real hourly wage has increased.

The Cyclical Pattern. Superimposed on the long-run downward trend of the workweek is a distinct cyclical pattern. As demand changes, production can be adjusted through some combination of employment and hours changes. The initial response is likely to be primarily in additional hours. When the economy turns down, costly overtime hours can be eliminated quickly and work schedules can be reduced to conform to production needs.

In the long recovery period since early 1961 the workweek for production workers in manufacturing increased steadily until the annual average for 1964 was as high as it had been in any year since 1945. This was true in spite of the fact that the unemployment rate in 1964 was substantially higher than in either 1955 or 1952, when the manufacturing workweek equaled the 1964 figure. Overtime hours in manufacturing climbed sharply at the beginning of the recovery, remained relatively steady until mid-1964, and then started to climb to record levels. The increase in the workweek and overtime hours received part of the blame for the fact that the unemployment rate declined very slowly as the economy continued its gradual recovery through 1964. It was argued that employers

found it less costly to increase production by increasing the workweek
and using overtime than by hiring new employees.

On the basis of available evidence, what can we say about whether or
not hours of work and overtime patterns have shifted relative to economic activity? It appears that the workweek is somewhat higher now
than the level that would be expected on the basis of past experience.
There seems to have been a shift in the hours-employment rate relationship in 1960–61 when the workweek was not reduced as much as might
have been anticipated on the basis of past experience. In addition, as
the current expansion extended beyond the first year, there was no reduction in the manufacturing workweek or overtime use, as seems to
have been the pattern in the past.

The Impact of Part-Time Work. In recent years, particularly outside
of manufacturing, the hours of work data may overstate the extent to
which the long-run downward trend in the workweek has continued. As
Henle pointed out, "Since part-time workers have been forming a considerably higher portion of the labor force, the figures for all workers
exaggerate the trend toward a shorter workweek."[1] In 1955 voluntary
part-time workers[2] made up about 8.3 per cent[3] of all those employed in
nonagricultural industries. By 1964 this figure had reached 11.7 per cent.
Sixty-five per cent of this part-time working force is female. A higher proportion of teen-agers of both sexes (72 per cent for boys and 77 per cent
for girls) are voluntary part-time workers, and a relatively high proportion of men and women over 65 (30.7 per cent and 42.5 per cent, respec-
tively) are part of this voluntary part-time work force. The increasing
fraction of the work force in this category automatically tends to reduce
the average number of hours worked in the economy. The shift to
voluntary part-time work more than explains the reduction in the workweek from 1959 to 1964. As we increase the normal period of schooling,
as the labor force participation rate of women increases, and as retirement becomes more attractive for workers in their later years, we can
expect the part-time work force to grow in relative importance.

[1] Peter Henle, "Recent Growth of Paid Leisure for U.S. Workers," *Monthly Labor
Review* (March 1962).

[2] Workers who usually work part time and worked part time during the survey week
for noneconomic reasons (e.g., did not want full-time work, too busy with school
and housework).

[3] Seasonally adjusted monthly average for the months May-December 1955.

OVERTIME HOURS

In May of 1964 nearly 15¾ million wage and salary single-job holders worked forty-one or more hours. They represented one out of every four single-job holders. Over 7 million of them worked forty-nine hours or more in the survey week. These figures represent a tempting target for those who believe that overtime hours can be translated into jobs.

It has frequently been asserted by proponents of a higher overtime penalty rate that the time-and-a-half provision for overtime no longer serves as an effective deterrent. This argument assumes that the gradual increase in the cost of fringe benefits, particularly those that are employee rather than hours-of-work costs, have reached a point where in many cases it is now less expensive to work overtime at the 50 per cent penalty rate than to hire a new employee.

On the basis of available evidence it seems unlikely that increases in fringe benefits are significantly related to any change in the use of overtime hours that may have occurred in the past few years. Under some circumstances it may be less expensive to schedule overtime than to hire employees for relatively short periods of time, but there is little evidence that total "turnover costs" have increased more rapidly in the last decade than the wage rates on which overtime penalties are based. There is no data on the amount of overtime that is "unavoidable." However, the use of substantial amounts of overtime in recession periods, and the fact that in many of the circumstances that lead to overtime, increasing employment is not a practical short-run alternative, warrant a presumption that an increase in the overtime penalty rate would have very little short-run impact on employment. In particular industries an increase in the marginal cost of overtime scheduling might lead to an increase in employment, but such a conclusion should be based on detailed industry studies of overtime experience.

In attempting to increase employment opportunities, serious consideration should be given to changing public and private policies that discourage or raise the costs of employment as well as to the possibility of making overtime less attractive. Increasing the overtime penalty rate would undoubtedly cut down on the amount of overtime scheduled. But as long as the alternative costs are high, there is little reason to expect a parallel increase in employment, at least in the short run.

Effects of the FLSA. In assessing the possible effect on overtime hours of an increase in the overtime penalty rate, it seems appropriate to raise the question of the effectiveness of the overtime penalty rates established by the Fair Labor Standards Act in 1938. It is somewhat embarrassing to have to admit that it is virtually impossible to demonstrate that the Fair Labor Standards Act has had a substantial effect on overtime hours worked or on the average workweek. All the evidence available is indirect. In 1938, when the Fair Labor Standards Act was passed, the average workweek was substantially below the forty-hour standard which was not to take effect until 1940. The workweek started to increase in 1938 and continued to increase for six years after the Fair Labor Standards Act was passed. Indeed, the clearest effect of the overtime penalty rates established by the law was to provide an effective means of attracting workers to war plants without increasing base rates. In many industries the pattern set in the war years has continued, and overtime hours are used to attract and reward employees. The continuing problem, shared by unions and management, of trying to allocate available overtime equitably among employees provides work opportunities for many arbitrators.

The Employment Potential of Reducing Overtime. Is there any potential for increasing employment by reducing overtime hours? We have already discussed a variety of factors that would make it extremely difficult and very costly to translate certain kinds of overtime into employment in the short run. However, given a sufficient adjustment period, there is little question that increasing the cost of overtime will induce employers to find new ways to avoid overtime penalties, and that some of these adjustments will involve substitution of employment for long workweeks. It is, therefore, appropriate to examine present overtime patterns for their employment potential.

In May 1964 over a million workers were putting in substantial amounts of overtime on a regular basis, in spite of the applicable overtime penalty rates. Whether the overtime hours by this group represent a realistic employment potential cannot be answered except in terms of particular industrial conditions. The costs of changing facilities, the feasibility of improving long-run projections of production requirements, and the alternatives available to employers are among the factors that would determine the rate of substitution of employment for overtime if the overtime penalty rate was increased. The experience in the retail trade industry is somewhat discouraging. In spite of a substantial amount of overtime in 1962, the subsequent imposition of overtime penalty rates did not create increased opportunities for regular employment. Since the impact of an increased overtime penalty rate would vary substantially among industries, and the extent to which the avowed employment objective might be accomplished would differ greatly among industries, an over-all increase in the overtime penalty rate would not seem appropriate. The costs in some sectors could far outweigh the possible benefits in others. Furthermore, since the employees in a given industry may have to bear a substantial part of the burden of increasing the overtime penalty rate in the form of reduced real earnings or inconvenient shifts and workweeks, there is a strong argument in favor of permitting flexible arrangements based on the preferences of the parties concerned. A decision process which considers employee attitudes toward income, work schedules, and employment, as well as employer estimates of the costs of the various alternatives, is more likely to avoid costly constraints that have no realistic potential for job creation.

MOONLIGHTING AS A SOURCE OF EMPLOYMENT OPPORTUNITY

Another group often looked to as a source of new jobs is the moonlighter. In May of 1964 there were 3.7 million persons, 5.2 per cent of all employed persons, with two jobs or more. Over a million of these workers held one of their jobs in agriculture, and a substantial number were self-employed either in their first or second jobs. However, after subtracting these there remain almost 2 million wage and salary workers who held two jobs in nonagricultural industries. Were these moonlighters taking up jobs that could have been filled by the unemployed?

Although moonlighting may be a significant factor in some sectors of the labor force, the practice cannot be blamed for the relatively high unemployment rates we have had in the last eight years. The number of individuals with more than one job has remained relatively stable since 1956, and the fraction of employment represented by dual job holders is about the same today as in 1957. It is probably academic to consider moonlighting jobs as a possible source of additional job opportunities. It is difficult to envisage a public policy that could be effective in reducing the practice.

THE SHORTER WORK WEEK

Another popular proposal for increasing job opportunities which has not lost its appeal is the shorter workweek. As far back as the 1880s and as recently as this year labor leaders have argued that a shorter workweek would provide more opportunities for their members. The claim has a great deal of common sense appeal, since it is apparent to all that if our present work force put in the same hours as workers did in the 1890s, our present level of demand could support only a fraction of the labor force. In spite of the obvious nature of this fallacy and of the unmistakable fact that the long-run reduction in the workweek has not reduced unemployment over the years, the belief that a shorter workweek will increase employment has not disappeared.

There is no question that work sharing can give workers more employment at lower average workweeks. Cost increases associated with scheduling problems aside for the moment, this simply means that a larger number of workers can produce a given output at approximately the same cost if they share the working hours utilized in the production process.

But work sharing at stable hourly wage rates is not the program that labor leaders have in mind when they assert they must fight for a reduced workweek in order to alleviate the unemployment problems in their industries. What they do have in mind is a reduced workweek at the same weekly pay. This is, of course, the equivalent of a substantial increase in wages, the amount depending upon the extent of the hours reduction. If the workweek is shortened without a reduction in the weekly wage, the unit cost of production will be increased in proportion to the rise in labor cost.

The proponents of shorter hours argue that the hours reduction without a reduction in weekly pay will automatically create the demand to increase employment. This "raise the economy by its bootstraps" argument ignores two critical issues. First of all, even if it would work exactly as argued, the higher prices required by the increased labor costs would imply a reduced real income for the originally employed labor force. Thus, the curtain of inflation would be used to disguise an over-all work-sharing policy. Of even greater importance is the shaky assumption that over-all demand will automatically increase enough to purchase the total product at the higher price level. Total private demand is made up of consumption and investment. There seems a high probability that the kind of pressure on costs and profits implied by the shorter-hour proposal would reduce, rather than increase, total demand.

Legislation might force a reduction of the workweek, and collective bargaining might preserve real weekly earnings, but employers will hire additional workers only if it is profitable to do so. Real incomes are determined by production, so that in the absence of an increase in labor productivity, reduced hours of work must mean less real income for someone. This will be true whether or not demand can be increased to provide jobs for new employees. There is no apparent way that a shorter workweek can produce an over-all increase in employment without some form of work and income sharing.

It has been argued that the increased costs associated with the reduced workweek would not materialize because labor productivity would increase as hours decline, thus preventing an increase in unit labor costs. Aside from the fact that the available evidence does not support the claim that hours reductions from the present levels would increase labor productivity enough to forestall a reduction in output and an increase in labor costs, the argument defeats its own purpose. If it were true that productivity would increase enough so that the same labor force could produce a given output in a shorter workweek, there would be no basis left for believing that a reduction in hours would increase employment. The current demand would provide for the same level of employment as before.

In short, one can say that employment can be increased if a way can be found to spread a given amount of production over a larger work force. However, in order to accomplish this, those who were employed prior to the change would, necessarily, on the average, have to accept a lower level of real income. Even work-spreading of this kind may not be successful if the process leads to a cost squeeze on employers, which in turn causes a reduction in investment spending, demand, and real output. Any increase in labor productivity associated with a reduction in hours would alleviate the cost impact, but to the same extent, would reduce the employment-creating potential of the workweek reduction. In the world of work, as elsewhere, there is no such thing as a free lunch. In order to increase job opportunities without reducing the real incomes of presently employed workers, there must be an increase in the demand for real goods and services. This is a necessary condition, whether or not the workweek is reduced, and whether or not employed workers take a fraction of their increased productivity in the form of greater leisure. While small groups of workers can increase their job opportunities at the expense of other workers and the economy in the short run, the only way a reduction in the workweek could stimulate employment over-all would be through a reduction in real income of presently employed workers.

New Directions in Aid of the Poor

by Sar A. Levitan, The W.E. Upjohn Institute for Employment Research

> *If to do were as easy as to know what were good to do, chapels had been churches, and poor men's cottages princes' palaces.*
> WILLIAM SHAKESPEARE

> *The needy shall not always be forgotten; the expectation of the poor shall not perish forever.*
> PSALMS 1:18

Public programs in aid of the poor in the United States carry an annual price tag of about $13 to $15 billion. Private philanthropic efforts on behalf of the poor raise the total funds allocated in their aid by about another billion dollars.

The rough estimate of resources allocated to the poor on the basis of need helps to lend perspective to the recently much-heralded commitment for a war on poverty embodied in the Economic Opportunity Act of 1964. Assuming that all the funds appropriated under this legislation actually reach the poor—a questionable assumption—the Economic Opportunity Act increased the antipoverty funds by about 5 per cent during its first year of activity; this amount was doubled during the second year.

It would be misleading, however, to measure the war on poverty solely in terms of direct expenditures. Minimum wage legislation, to which no price tag can be attached, may be a more significant tool in the war on poverty than the expenditures of billions under other programs, but its negative effect in causing disemployment cannot be measured. Some programs that may bring the greatest returns in the war on poverty may require little or practically no financial resources. Chief among these programs is an educational campaign to reduce, and possibly obliterate, discrimination practiced against minorities, particularly Negroes. The Voting Rights Act of 1965 may turn out to be a more important tool to secure equal rights for Negroes and thus to combat discrimination and poverty than other legislation involving huge expenditures.

Alternative Income Support Programs

Public assistance is currently the primary vehicle for transmitting aid to the poor. The income support provided is inadequate to meet basic needs of recipients, and even this support tends to discourage initiative because benefits are based on a stringent means test. Except for minor exemptions, earnings by relief recipients are normally deducted from benefits they receive, thus creating an incentive for the beneficiaries to withdraw from the labor force. Moreover, the majority of needy persons do not receive any assistance, and nearly four of every five poor persons do not receive public assistance. The federal government shares the cost of public assistance to selected groups—aged, blind, permanently disabled, and families with dependent children. States and local governments provide some assistance to needy persons outside these categories. But in many areas the destitute depend on private charity or have no support at all.

An additional problem of public assistance programs is that they have limited applicability to the working poor. Related programs intended to aid workers in the labor force, employed as well as unemployed, tend to bypass most of the poor, yet minimum wage legislation has raised the level of income of many working poor. The result of these inadequacies is that 2 million family heads (in 1963) having full-time year-round jobs received earnings insufficient to raise them above the poverty threshold.

FAMILY ALLOWANCES

While the acceptance of the principle of equal pay for equal work is desirable as a means of eliminating discrimination based on color or sex, it ignores the needs of families with children and tends to deprive children of large families of basic needs. The underlying justification for family allowances is that the well-being of children should be the concern of society as a whole. Family allowances also recognize that the wage system alone is an inadequate basis for distribution of income.

Providing minimum family needs under the wage system is an age-old problem which has occupied policy-makers since the early days of the industrial revolution. It was tried first on a modest basis in England 170 years ago and has spread widely during recent decades. It is now practiced, under one form or another, by most industrial countries. Family allowances are given in all European countries and in about a third of the nations outside Europe. In several countries these allowances account for a significant share of the total income received by families whose heads are low-wage earners and by families without breadwinners.

The family allowance programs for minimum needs in France and Canada illustrate two diverse types of systems. In France it is estimated that for a family of five, including three children, family allowances amount to about a quarter of total average wages paid in manufacturing; for a family with five children, the family allowances would add about two thirds to the average wages earned in manufacturing. Family allowances in France are financed by employers and amount to 13.5 per cent of total payrolls. In Canada, by contrast, family allowances are paid by the government from the general revenue. The monthly allowance amounts to $6 (Canadian) for each child under ten years of age and $8 for each child between the ages of ten and sixteen. Thus, the Canadian family allowances supply an insignificant proportion of total family income.

Our wage system is not adapted to take account of the diverse needs of workers, except for some adjustments in income taxes; for example, the take-home pay from two identical jobs is the same for a bachelor as for the head of a family with dependents. Despite the wide acceptance of the family allowance principle in other countries, the idea has never received active consideration in the United States—though it has been advanced on numerous occasions.[1] An exception has been made under AFDC for most needy children. Expenditures under this program account for 0.3 per cent of national income. A number of countries spend ten times this percentage or more of their national income for family allowances. France, for example, allocates about 5 per cent of national income to family allowances. And the trend in these countries has been to raise the proportion of national income devoted to family allowances.

NEGATIVE INCOME TAX

With the current commitment to wage war on poverty, various proposals have been advanced to supply additional income for the poor. The ultimate goal of these proposals is to raise the income of the poor and to eliminate poverty. The Social Security Administration has estimated that the addition of $11.5 billion would permit the 34.6 million persons designated as poor in 1963 to escape poverty.

[1]Paul H. Douglas, in *Wages and the Family* (Chicago: University of Chicago Press, 1925), advocated a family allowance system financed by employers. The late Senator Richard L. Neuberger of Oregon, a more recent advocate, proposed a Senate study of the feasibility of family allowances. His resolution (S. Res. 109, 84th Cong., 2d sess.) was cosponsored by seven other senators, including Paul H. Douglas, Hubert H. Humphrey, and John F. Kennedy; but it never received a hearing.

The most widely discussed proposal is utilization of the income tax machinery as a vehicle to supply income to the poor. The law, providing now only for the collection of taxes, might be extended to include grants based on family or individual needs. Prof. Robert J. Lampman of Wisconsin University has prepared the most careful and detailed cost estimates of different types of negative income tax proposals. The cost estimates presented in this section are based on Lampman's calculations.[2]

In its simplest form, a negative income tax would allow nontaxable individuals or families to claim the unused portion of their current exemptions. Such a plan would tend to spread the benefits thinly among most of the poor, but would still cost about $2 billion. If it were limited to families with children, the cost would be reduced by about one half. A family of four with zero income would be entitled to a "rebate" of $420. An "average" AFDC family—a mother with three children—would receive somewhat more than $200 in addition to the nearly $1500 of AFDC benefits, assuming that the states will continue current levels of assistance.

At the other extreme, negative income tax proposals would overhaul the present tax system to pay the poor enough income to close the poverty income gap which, as stated, amounted to $11.5 billion in 1963. Poverty would thus be eliminated. A workable plan would permit low-wage earners to keep at least a portion of their earned income in order to provide them an incentive to continue working. This would, of course, increase the cost of the income maintenance program by a larger amount than the $11.5 billion poverty income gap. Lampman estimates that the cost of such a program would be double the present poverty income gap, or about $23 billion. This appears to be a conservative estimate.

A compromise between the above two plans would guarantee income to cover 50 per cent of the poverty income gap. Thus a family of four would receive a guaranteed annual income of $1565, based on the Social Security Administration estimates of basic needs. The cost of such a plan would be $8 billion. But this amount includes about $3 billion which is now currently paid to public assistance recipients. The net cost would, therefore, be about $5 billion. If the plan were limited to families with children, the cost would amount to $4.8 billion less the $1.3 billion now paid to public assistance recipients. As in the previous proposal, this

2"Approaches to the Reduction of Poverty," *Papers and Proceedings of the Seventy-seventh Annual Meeting of the American Economic Association*, (May 1965), pp. 521–29; "Income Distribution and Poverty," in Margaret S. Gordon, ed., *Poverty in America* (San Francisco: Chandler Publishing Co., 1965). pp. 102–14; and others which are now in press.

scheme would also have to provide for continued incentive to work and allow low-income earners to keep all or part of their earnings. The cost would therefore be raised appreciably above the estimated $5 billion.

The three variations of negative income tax schemes suggest the cost magnitude of any negative income tax plan. The three proposals listed above would incur annual costs ranging from $2 billion to $23 billion or higher. Different variations of these plans would involve a cost anywhere between these two extremes. Huge as these sums might appear, an addition of $5 to $23 billion to the income of the poor—ignoring the first scheme which would distribute the limited funds broadly—might be an attainable goal, given our society's present commitment to combat poverty. However, providing the poor with added income is only one aspect of combating poverty. The poor also need better schools, housing, training, and diverse services to improve their ability to compete for jobs in the labor market. Any adequate public welfare system, whose goal is to reduce poverty, must therefore aim at a judicious distribution of resources, both for raising the income level of the poor and for providing them with needed services.

COMPETING GOALS

The goal of eliminating poverty is only one of many aspirations of our society which involve substantial financial resources.

It is not likely that society will decide in the foreseeable future to allocate the resources needed to win total victory over poverty, nor would excessive reliance upon transfer payments appear to constitute sound public policy. While allocation of additional income for the poor is an essential element in the war on poverty, simply raising income to fill even their minimum requirements would result in economic dislocations by eroding incentives to work. It may also be preferable in many cases to stress income in kind rather than in cash. This might apply to alcoholics and others afflicted with diverse maladjustments.

It is apparent that the waging of a successful war on poverty is a complex and costly undertaking. Even the 89th Congress, which is generally acknowledged as being the most welfare-conscious Congress in more than a generation, has not shown any inclination to commit the necessary resources to eliminate poverty in the immediate years ahead. It has been particularly parsimonious in allocating additional income to the poor. Only about 2 per cent ($150 million) of the multibillion-dollar 1965 amendments to the Social Security Act were allocated to raising federal contributions to public assistance. Nor has the administration, which is committed to a total war on poverty, urged Congress to adopt programs which would raise the income level of the poor in the immediate years ahead. Whatever may be the merits of the varied income maintenance programs discussed above, there does not appear to be any wide consensus supporting their adoption. Although such a plan might receive serious consideration at some indeterminate future, to improve the lot of the poor in the short run we must realistically turn to more modest programs.

Short-Run Priorities

Michael S. March, one of the administration's early architects of the current poverty program, has stated:

> Poverty has a formidable ally in our own ignorance of what we must do to root out poverty. When one stands "eyeball to eyeball" with poverty, preparing for mortal struggle, he will admit, if he is candid, that he does not know exactly what is best to do or how to do it.
>
> There is a surprising dearth of hard knowledge about the root causes and dynamics of poverty. . . . Our prescriptions for the cure of poverty are unsure and lacking in consensus.[3]

Yet the significant gaps in our understanding of the causes of poverty and the best means for eradicating its roots are no valid reason, as March argues, for inaction. We need not await returns from all the precincts to continue a vigorous campaign to reduce poverty. Lacking comprehensive knowledge for eliminating the roots of poverty, we can focus on specific programs which would aid selected groups among the poor. This suggested emphasis upon helping specific groups is not intended to supplant the generalized societal goal of eliminating all poverty. A free and affluent society should aim at nothing less. But we should realize this is an ultimate goal and only one among numerous and pressing demands upon society's attentions and resources. For the time being, more modest and specialized strategems should be selected with a view to achieving the ultimate objective. Grand designs for the good society have been avoided, not only because there is little evidence that society is ready to allocate adequate resources to a speedy reduction of poverty and because of the many pressing and competing goals faced by society, but also because the road leading to the millennium of a poorless society is not fully charted.

Even assuming that consensus can be reached on the amount of additional resources that need to be allocated for the war on poverty, it is

[3] "Poverty: How Much Will the War Cost?" *Social Service Review* (June 1965), pp. 154–55.

not at all clear how these resources should be distributed. What share of any additional dollar should be allocated to raising the cash income of the poor as compared with improving the quality and quantity of services in kind? The poor are not a homogeneous mass. Additional income will provide for the basic needs of some; many others require services to enable them to enter the mainstream of our society. Until these special services and income in kind are adequate, it is premature to hope to achieve a rational guaranteed level of acceptable minimum income—whether this is to be achieved through negative income tax or other similar schemes.

Major steps have been taken during the past year in the difficult and long journey whose goal is a poorless society. Whether all the programs will advance the journey is not yet known. The new antipoverty and related programs have strained the limited technical resources in the areas of social services and training. However, new programs and techniques developed by the Office of Economic Opportunity may provide for more efficient utilization of existing resources. For example, Head Start utilized unused school resources during the summer of 1965. Similarly, various projects stressing participation by the poor may expand services with hitherto unutilized resources. Judicious allocation of resources would suggest, however, the need of appraising the newly sponsored programs before additional funds are made available to OEO. The expected expansion in demand of medical care provided for in the 1965 legislation will more than exhaust available medical facilities and services. Any further major attempt to expand medical services to the poor during the next few years would, therefore, mean the redistribution of existing resources rather than an expansion of aggregate services.

A realistic program aimed at reducing poverty should therefore establish priorities and determine appropriate resources to be allocated. Leaving aside rhetoric about the elimination of poverty, it is assumed here that if society continues to increase resources allocated for alleviating poverty, say, at the cumulative rate of about 6 to 7 per cent per year—about half as much as the anticipated growth of GNP—this would increase the antipoverty kitty by about $4 billion per year by the end of this decade. Given this modest, though far from negligible, short-term goal, the immediate question is which existing or new programs should claim priority for the additional resources.

Looking to the future, the most promising means of reducing poverty is to help the poor control the size of their families, a goal which can be achieved at negligible cost to the public. Primary emphasis should be placed on helping the impoverished to plan parenthood and thus reduce the number of unwanted children. However, the largest amount of expanded assistance would go to aid poor children, and to help create jobs for their parents.

It makes little sense to wage war on poverty without providing an adequate diet and other basic needs for millions of children who are being reared with an insufficient income. To repeat the social worker's slogan: "Services do not fill an empty stomach." Most observers would, however, agree that it would be preferable to provide income to impoverished families through the creation of jobs rather than through providing cash assistance. This would suggest the desirability of creating publicly subsidized jobs for parents of poor children, even though the creation of such employment may involve greater direct public outlays than mere cash assistance. Finally, in the area of providing goods to the poor, housing should claim top priority, not only because attainment of adequate shelter is outside the reach of most poor families but because outlays for subsidized housing would also help absorb general economic slack.

PLANNED PARENTHOOD

> *The problem, everyone talks of it, is that of birth control. . . . It is an extremely grave problem. It touches on the mainsprings of human life.*

POPE PAUL VI

The first priority in the war on poverty should be given to dissemination of education about methods of birth control, and, consistent with the religious beliefs of recipients, assistance should be made available to those who cannot afford private medical aid to plan parenthood. No major religious group in the United States is opposed to regulation of family size, though differences do exist on the methods permissible to achieve this goal and on the appropriate role of the state in this area. But without entering into the theological aspects of the birth control controversy, the views of Richard Cardinal Cushing are pertinent for the purposes of this discussion. He recognized the necessity for the state to follow, on occasion, a path which may differ from the views of a religious group, when he stated:

> Catholics do not need the support of civil law to be faithful to their religious convictions, and they do not seek to impose by law their moral views on other members of society.[4]

[4]U.S. Congress, Senate Committee on Government Operations, Subcommittee on Foreign Aid Expenditures, hearings, June 22, 1965, 89th Congress, 1st sess., on S. 1676 and related bills (Washington: U.S. Government Printing Office, 1965).

However, the official Catholic position on birth control remains unchanged. In October 1965, Pope Paul VI addressed the United Nations urging the representatives of the nations:

> You must strive to multiply bread so that it suffices for the tables of mankind, and not rather favor an artificial control of birth which would be irrational, in order to diminish the number of guests at the banquet of life.[5]

Broad support exists for dissemination of birth control information. In reply to a recent Gallup poll question: "Do you favor or oppose the distribution of birth control information?" no less than 80 per cent of Protestants, 60 per cent of Catholics, and 84 per cent of other religious groups answered in the affirmative.

With regard to the role of birth control in combating poverty, former President Eisenhower expressed the prevailing general attitude about federal support of birth control when he wrote:

> I realize that in important segments of our people and of other nations this question is regarded as a moral one and therefore scarcely a fit subject for federal legislation. With their feelings I can and do sympathize. But I cannot help believe that the prevention of human degradation and starvation is likewise a moral—as well as a material—obligation resting upon every enlightened government. If we now ignore the plight of those unborn generations which, because of our unreadiness to take corrective action in controlling population growth, will be denied any expectations beyond abject poverty and suffering, then history will rightly condemn us.[6]

One of the most tragic aspects of poverty is that many of the children born to poor families are unwanted. The National Academy of Sciences concluded that the poor have more children than affluent families because the poor "do not have the information or the resources to plan their families effectively according to their own desires."[7] The same study found that 17 per cent of white couples and 31 per cent of nonwhite couples had unwanted children in 1960. But among couples with least education, and thus also likely to be poor, the comparative percentages were 32 per cent for white couples and 43 per cent for nonwhite couples.

Medical science has developed effective birth control methods that are within the means of poor families. Given the widespread desire on the part of poor parents to regulate the size of their families, birth control could be used as an effective tool to reduce future poverty. It is important that information about these methods and the necessary devices

---

[5]"Consensus Grows on Birth Control," *Business Week,* (Oct. 9, 1965), p. 36.

[6]Hearings on S. 1676 and related bills, *op. cit.*

[7]National Academy of Sciences, *The Growth of U.S. Population* (Washington: The Academy, 1965), p. 10.

be made available to the general public without further delay because children born during the "baby boom" years are marrying and planning the size of their families. In 1960 there were 4.7 million women aged 18 to 21. Five years later their number increased to 6 million, and by 1968 it is expected that this figure will increase by another million.

With minor exceptions, federal agencies have thus far avoided the funding of birth control programs. Even the Office of Economic Opportunity has shunned this controversial area. Only about 1 per cent of the first one thousand OEO-backed community action programs carried specific budgets for birth control programs.

It may be expected that the federal government will offer more positive support of birth control in the future. Katherine B. Oettinger, Chief, Children's Bureau, Department of Health, Education, and Welfare, declared recently that birth control services should be available to all as a matter of "right."

> . . . for it is the families of the poor who too long have suffered spiritual dejection and demoralization after bearing successive babies without hope of these children being able to achieve their full potential or breaking the cycle of poverty.[8]

Potentially more effective support of birth control programs came from President Johnson when he stated on June 25, 1965: "Let us act on the fact that less than $5 invested in population control is worth $100 invested in economic growth." The President did not specify the basis on which he made his estimates, but ample evidence exists to indicate the savings that accrue to the public as a result of family-planning services. For example, a birth control program initiated in Mecklenburg County, N.C., in 1960 was estimated to have saved $250,000 in AFDC benefits within three years. Expenses involved in operating the program amounted to one twentieth of the savings. Many other examples could be cited. The arithmetic is simple. Even considering the low cost of AFDC support, averaging just about a dollar a day, the few dollars expended per case on birth control saves the government the cost of supporting an AFDC child for years to come, not to mention that it also reduces poverty.

AIDING IMPOVERISHED CHILDREN

> *The child was diseased at birth, stricken with heriditary ill that only the most vital men are able to shake off. I mean poverty— the most deadly and prevalent of all diseases.*
>
> EUGENE O'NEILL

[8]Katherine B. Oettinger, "This Most Profound Challenge," *Congressional Record* (daily edition), Sept. 24, 1965, p. 24201.

If the current battle cry "break the chains of poverty" is not to become a hollow slogan, society must allocate additional resources to prevent the rearing of children in abject poverty and deprivation. The child from an impoverished home is likely to become a school dropout, an unemployable adult, and a perpetual relief recipient. Therefore, the next priority for any increased allocation of funds should go to helping poor children.

Though in need of radical overhauling, the AFDC program provides a suitable vehicle for this purpose. The nearly 1 million families, with about 3 million children, who are currently recipients of AFDC are among the neediest and most impoverished in the United States; therefore, they deserve the most immediate attention. The average income paid by the government to AFDC recipients is about $1 a day. Since the minimum cost of food for a balanced diet is 70 cents per person per day and accounts for only a third of the basic needs, it is quite apparent that AFDC children exist on an inadequate diet, even if total food costs of young children are somewhat lower than the 70-cent average.

Before AFDC can be adopted as the main instrument for a decent relief system and as a rehabilitation tool, the program will have to be overhauled. Not only must the level of allowances paid to recipients be increased, but the method of distribution will have to be changed. The Veterans Administration pension system, described earlier, should be adopted as a model, since the VA experience has shown that the government can offer assistance to needy persons without subjecting them to harassment or degradation. And, unlike the AFDC program, the Veterans Administration does not discourage initiative of recipients.

In most states earnings received by members of AFDC families are deducted from the total allowances the family is entitled to receive, allowing only minimal exemptions. The Economic Opportunity Act provides that the first $85 and half of additional monthly income earned under the provisions of the act (except work experience) are not to be counted as income for purposes of determining basic needs under public assistance programs. The 1965 amendments to the Social Security Act are less generous and permit states to disregard for purposes of benefit payments the monthly earnings of dependent children, not exceeding $50 per child or $150 per family. But the choice is left to each state; and if past experience is any indication of future action, most states are not likely to permit this exemption. In all but a few states the allowable exemption exceeds the total payments made by the state per child. AFDC as now operative in most states is not aimed at rehabilitating recipients or encouraging initiative and promoting self-respect. The resources of the system are concentrated on providing a substandard income, thereby leaving most recipients in abject poverty.

An effective AFDC program which does more than pay lip service to the rehabilitation of clients must also raise payments made to recipients. Even assuming that $600 per individual is the minimum income needed —and for a family of four this is 23 per cent below the social security poverty threshold level of income—it would be necessary to increase current benefits paid to AFDC recipients by about two thirds in order to reach this income level. This suggested figure takes account of free food distribution available to many AFDC recipients. Such a boost in the level of payments would also increase the number of eligible recipients. The few states which meet or approach the level of benefits suggested above would not have to raise their AFDC outlays.

To meet the proposed standards, AFDC expenditures would have to be raised by about a billion dollars. And expansion of coverage would possibly double the cost, though an effective birth control program would tend to reduce the number of children in impoverished households and decrease future costs. The 1965 social security amendments raise the maximum amount of federal contributions to AFDC recipients by only $15 a year, and state action to match these benefits is required before the increased federal grants can be paid to recipients. The miniscule increase in payments made possible by the 1965 federal action indicates the resistance that exists in Congress and elsewhere to higher AFDC payments. State and local resistance may be even more difficult to overcome. The federal share of contributions to AFDC will therefore have to be increased appreciably if an effective program is to materialize.

It makes little sense to spend $6000 a year, and possibly more, to rehabilitate a Job Corps trainee, while at the same time depriving children in impoverished homes of basic needs and thus assuring a supply of future Job Corps candidates. This is not to disparage the potential accomplishments of the Job Corps or other programs initiated under the Economic Opportunity Act, but it does suggest the serious gaps that now exist in the antipoverty program.

JOB CREATION AND WORK RELIEF

> *Anticipate charity by preventing poverty; assist the reduced fellowman . . . so that he may earn an honest livelihood, and not be forced to the dreadful alternative of holding out his hand for charity. This is the highest step and the summit of charity's golden ladder.* MOSES BEN MAIMON

Creation of jobs for which the poorly educated and unskilled would qualify is the third on our list of priorities. After almost complete neglect of work relief programs during the past two decades, the Economic

Opportunity Act provided for job creation under its work experience and youth employment programs. The continued high level of unemployment among the unskilled, particularly among Negroes, indicates the need for generating government-supported jobs for those who cannot qualify for gainful employment in private industry. This does not mean that the government should create make-work jobs.

Despite the gloomy forebodings of the prophets of cybernation, much of society's needed work is not being done, and the need is going to increase rather than disappear. Many of these jobs can be performed by relatively unskilled and unemployed workers. And the work can be found in rural areas and urban centers. Stream clearance, reforestation, and park maintenance are some of the simple traditional work relief jobs. Many new ones can be added, for example: school aids, health aids, simple maintenance jobs of public buildings, and renovation of slum areas. Medicare will not only expand the demand for services of physicians and technicians, but will also require the addition of many unskilled workers in hospitals and nursing homes.

The need for creating jobs for unskilled workers may become more pressing in the years ahead. Proposed congressional action boosting the statutory minimum wage by 75 per cent within a period of nine years, if it materializes in 1966, is likely to cause additional disemployment of unskilled workers. If no new jobs are created for these workers, relief will be the only method of providing income maintenance.

A major barrier to the creation of new public jobs for the unemployed is the determination of appropriate wage rates. Unions normally oppose the allocation of work, even when unskilled jobs are involved, at rates which undermine existing prevailing standards. Creation of these jobs is bound to be costly. A million dollars will buy no more than about three hundred jobs, including some part-time jobs, paying modest wages and including cost of overhead and equipment. A program which will create 300,000 jobs, not an overambitious goal, is thus going to cost about $1 billion annually.

HOUSING

> *They turn the needy out of way; the poor of the earth hide themselves together . . . and embrace the rock for want of a shelter.*
>
> Job 24:4–R

Housing for impoverished families is given high priority because it is evident that adequate shelter cannot be provided by private enterprise at a profit, considering the rent that they can pay. It thus meets the generally accepted maxim of Lincoln that "the legitimate object of government is to do for the people what needs to be done, but which they cannot, by individual effort, do at all, or do so well, for themselves." The alternative to government subsidization of housing for the poor is slums and dilapidated housing which, in turn, breed poverty. Adequate housing is, therefore, a major instrument in breaking the chains of poverty.

A continuing vigorous program of subsidized public housing would also act as an over-all economic stimulant which would help decrease unemployment and expand job opportunities. Such a program is, therefore, a multipurpose tool in fighting poverty.

The great shortage of adequate housing available to the poor cannot be surmounted in the short run. It would require, even under the most conservative estimates, an investment in excess of $30 billion to eliminate substandard housing. The principle of housing subsidies has already been accepted, as witnessed by congressional action in 1965. The question now is how rapidly the program is to be implemented. A constraining factor should be the extent to which underutilized resources, both human and physical, are available for the purpose of building housing. This is not to suggest that construction of housing for the poor is inherently of low priority compared with the supply of other consumer goods. Most consumer goods are produced in the free market and are not subject to government regulation. A vigorous implementation of public housing during a period of shortages would intensify inflationary pressures, particularly in the field of housing construction where boosts in wage costs have tended to exceed increases in productivity. Since construction of subsidized housing is subject to government control, the degree of priority assigned to this program is diminished if it is to be undertaken at the risk of intensifying inflationary pressures.

Under the conditions that prevailed in the country between 1958 and 1964, expansion of housing for the poor could have been vigorous and rapid. With developing labor shortages and increased commitments to expand defense activities, subsidized housing expansion must be more moderate and selective. However, the level of unemployment and the amount of utilized plant resources still remain high in many areas where additional construction activity could absorb some of the existing economic slack.

Since the supply of adequate housing for the poor will remain necessarily far short of need, priority in allocating the limited supply should be given to the working poor. This judgment is not based necessarily on the assumption that the working poor are more "deserving." It is advanced because pragmatic considerations favor the working poor for the allocation of subsidized housing. Public housing has been criticized on the basis that it subsidizes the indolent, but this argument could be minimized if the bulk of subsidized housing were allocated to the working poor. Even opponents of the welfare state find it difficult to argue against helping the "deserving" poor.

Is Business "As Usual" Feasible?

> *If there be among you a poor man. . . . thou shalt not harden thine heart, nor shut thine hand from thy poor brother . . . and shall surely lend him sufficient for his need, in that which he wanteth.*

DEUTERONOMY 15: 7–8

The cumulative addition of a billion dollars a year in aid of the poor during the next four years will only alleviate poverty for some, and large segments will hardly benefit by the programs outlined above. Included in these groups are more than 5 million persons aged 65 and over, and most of the 4 million families headed by gainfully employed, unemployed, or underemployed workers. The aged group has been aided by the passage of Medicare and the boost in social security benefits, but much more will have to be done to raise the income of the aged poor to the poverty threshold. To improve the lot of the poor in the work force, reliance is placed on the achievement of full employment, job creation, and protective wage legislation. The achievement of full employment is a *sine qua non* in the war on poverty; it is essential to the achievement of many of society's aspirations. Sustained full employment will not only absorb many of the unemployed poor in the work force but should also raise their level of income.

It would take the absorption of more than 3 million poor into the work force to achieve the same proportion of gainfully employed among the poor as among the nonpoor. Given the educational, demographic, and other impediments of the poor, such conditions cannot be achieved even with full employment. It is questionable whether sustained full employment can be maintained in the next few years—assuming that it will be achieved at all before the end of this decade.

In brief, the anticipated allocation of an additional $1 billion a year in aid of the poor assumes that society will stop short of assigning top priority to the war on poverty and that the goal of accelerating the reduction of poverty will remain one of several societal aspirations, competing for available limited resources. It represents only a modest effort in combating poverty and will result in little redistribution of income. It is not at all clear that such a situation will remain tenable in the years ahead in face of widespread Negro unrest and the commitment of the Great Society to eliminate poverty. Half of the Negro population lives in poverty, compared with one of every seven whites. It is likely that the civil rights movement is going to stress even more the attainment of broader economic opportunities for the Negro population. And recent incidents indicate that some sectors of the Negro population are not inclined to rely exclusively upon orderly procedures to achieve a greater measure of economic and political equality. Society may find it necessary, therefore, to allocate far greater resources in aid of the poor than was anticipated in this bulletin.

Manpower Adjustments to Automation and Technological Change in Western Europe

by Jack Stieber, Michigan State University

The objective of this study is to determine the attitudes towards automation and technological change in full employment economies, the manpower problems faced in such countries, and measures taken to deal with those problems. At the risk of oversimplification, we would say that the West European countries studied are interested in the positive effects of technological development, whereas up to now the United States has been concerned primarily with the negative aspects of automation and technological change. The major question posed in the full employment countries is: "How can we speed up technological development in order to increase productivity and the rate of economic growth?" In the United States the predominant question has been: "What is the effect of automation on unemployment and what can be done to minimize adverse effects on employees?"

This difference in attitudes reflects the different unemployment situation and manpower outlook in the United States and most of the countries in Western Europe. With a high rate of unemployment, a rapidly expanding labor force, and an economy undergoing rapid technological change, the United States must not only create a few million new jobs each year to reduce unemployment and absorb new entrants into the labor force and offset increasing productivity; it must also adjust the skills of its manpower to the requirements of a technologically advancing economy. The West European countries already have full—some of them overfull—employment and face a period of declining growth in their active populations during the next five years. Their problem is not one of job creation, but of job elimination. Their efforts are directed at the most efficient utilization of available labor supplies and drawing upon manpower reserves, wherever possible, to increase the size of their active populations.

Most of the countries studied are using both "push" and "pull" methods to achieve their economic objectives. Industry is being pushed by government to modernize, adopt advanced technology, locate in areas of labor surplus, and provide necessary training for their workers. Among the inducements offered to industry are subsidies, low-interest loans, tax allowances, compensation for costs of training manpower, and other financial incentives. At the same time, workers are being pulled toward greater acceptance of the adjustments required by rapid technological advance through a variety of measures which differ from country to country, and include relatively high levels of unemployment insurance, severance pay, generous retraining allowances, moving allowances, limited earnings guarantees, provisions for early retirement with liberal pensions, and, most important of all, a full employment economy which offers alternative job opportunities to those who need them.

There is a striking difference between Western Europe and the United States in the importance attached to full employment and even in the definition of the term. Full employment is endorsed as a top-priority policy goal not only by unions and government officials; it is accepted and supported by West European employers to a far greater extent than by their American counterparts. The necessity and propriety of government action to achieve or maintain rapid growth and full employment is accepted by unions and employers alike. Both are convinced that such action is in their best interest: unions because they want jobs for their members, and employers because they recognize the economic advantages in terms of their own profit-making potential.

Furthermore, full employment is defined much more stringently than in the United States: 2 to 2.5 per cent unemployment represents the outer limits of acceptability rather than the 3 to 4 per cent which is so widely accepted as consistent with a full employment economy in the United States. To start worrying about inflation and to take action to damp down the economy when unemployment was in excess of 4 per cent and prices were rising at an annual rate of less than 2 per cent would be inconceivable in the West European context.

Trade unions in the countries studied are less concerned over the impact of automation and changing technology than in the United States. Collective bargaining demands tend to stress such traditional issues as wages, hours, and vacations with pay, rather than job security. This reflects both an emphasis on priority issues and the feeling that government has the primary responsibility for protecting workers against unemployment and the adverse effects of technological change. Where job security issues have been injected into collective bargaining, they have centered on such subjects as extension of legal provisions for dismissal notice, advance consultation, severance pay, guarantees against loss of income in job transfers, early retirement for unemployed workers, retraining opportunities, and special provisions for older workers. On the whole, American unions have little to learn from their West European counterparts in the area of job security through collective bargaining.

The American system of industrial relations, by including detailed provisions regarding layoff and dismissal procedures in collective bargaining agreements, has avoided a problem that is found in several West European countries, where the order of dismissals is handled on an *ad hoc* basis. This often results in strikes and individual complaints when plant closures or economic conditions make layoffs necessary.

West European employers differ from their American counterparts in assuming a greater social obligation for providing continuous employment for their workers. This may extend to continuing to employ, or delaying dismissal of, workers who are no longer needed when alternative job opportunities are not readily available, and to helping find new jobs for employees about to be dismissed. There is also a greater acceptance by employers of government intervention in the labor market, as evidenced by the Redundancy Pay Act in Great Britain; the Industrial Training Act in Great Britain and the apprenticeship tax in France; regulation of collective dismissals in France, West Germany, and the Netherlands; individual dismissal notice requirements in all countries except Sweden; authority to compel employment of a specified percentage of handicapped workers in a few countries; and legal specifications of vacation benefits and limits on overtime work in some countries.

There appears to be a greater appreciation by West European employers of the perils that unemployment holds for the ordinary worker and a willingness to adopt a pragmatic solution even if it involves more government intervention than they consider desirable. This attitude is illustrated by the following comment by a British employer:

> We are out to make unemployment costless. We must have more flexibility in use of the work force. We want freedom to introduce technological change. To reduce resistance we must reduce fear. If we can make unemployment costless, people will not be afraid to become unemployed and therefore will not resist our efforts.

We have seen that all five of the countries studied have experienced significant changes in the structure of employment during the postwar years as a result of technological developments, the introduction of the Common Market, increased international competition, and other factors. The programs—old or new—employed to deal with manpower problems cannot generally be differentiated on the basis of the development that brought them into being, since the same program often serves more than one purpose.

In summarizing some of the programs in effect in West European countries, we proceed from the premise that while different labor market conditions may call for different approaches, these measures, with appropriate modifications to meet U.S. conditions, merit our consideration.

Dismissal Notice. Four of the five countries require employers to obtain prior approval or to give advance notification to the public employment service before dismissing workers for economic reasons. In addition, individual employees are entitled to receive dismissal notice of varying periods, depending upon length of service. At the very least, this calls for advance planning on the part of employers and assures that they will make reasonable efforts to avoid or minimize dismissals. In some situations dismissals can be delayed, extended over a period of time, or even canceled by the government. In the United States, there are no legal restrictions on an employer's right to lay off or dismiss workers when they are not needed. Although many collective bargaining agreements provide for notice prior to layoff, the time period involved is generally no more than a few days.

Removal Allowances. All five countries provide removal allowances of various kinds, usually administered by the government employment service, to promote geographical mobility from areas of surplus manpower to labor shortage areas. However, even in countries with rather liberal allowances, most workers who move do so without financial assistance from government. In the United States, the public employment service is not authorized to reimburse expenses of workers moving from one area to another to seek or accept employment. However, the Labor Department has engaged in some "demonstration" projects under which it has given relocation assistance in a limited number of areas. In addition, a few collective bargaining agreements provide for paying the cost of relocation. But these are exceptions, and practically all American workers who move to accept jobs must do so on their own.

Retraining.   Occupational mobility is encouraged in all countries by retraining programs which vary greatly as regards number and proportion of the labor force trained, types of courses offered, eligibility requirements, duration, and financial allowances to trainees. The United States has made rapid progress in training the unemployed under the Manpower Development and Training Act (MDTA). It is clear from European experiences that retraining is necessary in full employment economies as well as during periods of relatively high unemployment. The MDTA should be made permanent under legislation which will permit sufficient flexibility in its administration to adapt to the needs of the labor market. U.S. training allowances are much lower in relation to prevailing wage rates than allowances paid in the countries studied. As our unemployment situation improves, it will become more difficult to attract unemployed workers into courses and to keep them from dropping out before completion to accept jobs which may not be related to their training. This has been the experience of other countries even though their training allowances are more closely related to prevailing wage levels.

Some of the unusual features of retraining programs in other countries might also be tried in this country: for example, the West German program, which refunds part of the wages paid by employers giving training to formerly unemployed workers; or the Dutch arrangement for subsidizing employers training unemployed workers for the difference in productivity of such trainees and fully trained workers. Many other features which might be worthy of experimentation are included in Dr. Gordon's excellent study of retraining in Western Europe.[1]

The Employment Service.   There is wide variation among countries in the role played by the public employment service. The best, as epitomized by the Federal Institute for Placement and Unemployment Insurance in West Germany and the National Labor Market Board in Sweden, are far superior to the U.S. Employment Service. On the other hand, our own system is probably on a par with or better than those

[1]M. S. Gordon, "Income Security Programs and the Propensity To Retire," Reprint No. 210, Institute of Industrial Relations, University of California, Berkeley, 1963.

found in the other countries. The one respect in which the United States differs from all five countries is in permitting private profit-making agencies to operate along with the public employment service. In none of the countries studied are agencies operated for profit permitted, except by special licensing or on a "temporary basis."

Industrial Location. Great Britain and France control the location of new industrial facilities in order to keep new plants out of congested areas and to persuade them to locate in areas with relatively high unemployment. All countries try to influence location decisions by offering various inducements to locate in certain areas as opposed to others. There is a trend towards identifying and concentrating on "growth" or "development" centers rather than promoting industrial location in all areas of labor surplus. There is considerable difference of opinion regarding the long-term advantages and disadvantages of industrial location policies. The argument sometimes takes the form of debating the relative merits of moving workers and moving jobs. The latter appears to be getting more emphasis at this time. There is a need for more research to determine the costs and benefits of government programs to influence industrial location.

Unemployment Insurance. Systems for compensating unemployed workers differ from country to country and are difficult to compare. It would appear, however, that the U.S. unemployment insurance system, in terms of average benefits in relation to earnings and in duration of payments, is substantially inferior to the systems in West Germany and the Netherlands, about on a par with that in Sweden, and not much, if at all, better than those in Great Britain and France. Unemployed workers in the Common Market countries who meet specified requirements are also eligible to receive special allowances paid by the European Social Fund and the European Coal and Steel Community. The level of unemployment benefits takes on added importance because it is often used as a yardstick in setting training allowances in the United States and other countries.

Old-Age Pensions. In four of the five countries—Great Britain is the exception—eligibility for old-age pensions is not dependent upon whether or not one continues to work. In the United States there is a limit on permissible earnings of pensioners up to age 72. It would seem that the U.S. policy would discourage persons over 65 from continuing to work, while the West European countries' policy should have the opposite effect. However, the statistics on men and women over 65 in the labor force show that we have a higher participation rate for such persons than any of the countries studied. This may indicate that our old-age benefits are lower in relation to earnings before retirement and/or need than those in other countries. Or it may merely reflect differences in custom or social values on the subject of older people working. Old-age pensions in all the countries, except Great Britain, are adjusted regularly for changes in the cost of living or in wages, which are used as a base for determining pensions. A few countries have provisions for early retirement with little or no reduction in pensions, or for special payments to workers over 60 who have been unemployed for a certain period of time.

We are not prepared to say which, if any, of the policies followed in other countries should be adopted by our own government, with or without modification. These are fit subjects for consideration by the Commission, the Executive branch, and the Congress.

In one area—research on manpower problems—the United States is acknowledged to be far ahead of Western Europe. In every country, professionals working in the manpower field praised both the quality and quantity of research by U.S. government agencies and universities as compared with the relatively meager resources devoted to manpower research in their own countries. They were particularly impressed with the tendency to include budget items for evaluation purposes in legislation authorizing new programs. Efforts are being made in a few countries to persuade government departments concerned with manpower to follow the U.S. example with respect to evaluation research as well as manpower research in general.

In conclusion we should like to raise briefly two questions which, we think, merit further consideration.

It would appear that the high premium placed upon continued employment and avoiding or delaying layoffs and dismissals in some of the countries studied must result in some overmanning, inefficiencies in the production process, and higher unit labor costs. Whatever the social value of such policies, it is doubtful whether they are desirable or appropriate from an economic point of view. However, if we opt for having economic decisions in the firm made solely on economic grounds, as we have in the United States, we should recognize that the workers laid off with little or no advance notice are contributing indirectly to the increased efficiency of our firms. This recognition would indicate a policy of relatively liberal unemployment insurance benefits, generous retraining allowances, and other measures to ease the plight of the unemployed and help them to find employment as soon as possible.

But what do we find? Not only do we follow policies which take no account of the special hardships on employees who are laid off or dismissed with little or no advance notice, but we are also less liberal in the treatment of our unemployed and adult trainees than other countries. It hardly seems justifiable to make the unemployed pay twice for the increased efficiency which benefits everybody but themselves.

The other question relates to the great emphasis which is presently being placed on the high school dropout problem in the United States. In none of the countries visited did we find a similar concern over youths who had not had the equivalent of a high school education, despite the fact that a much higher proportion of 15 to 19 year-olds are in the labor force everywhere than in the United States. In 1958, 66 per cent of our youths aged 15 to 19 were in school, as compared with about 30 per cent in France, Sweden, and the Netherlands, and only 18 per cent in Great Britain and West Germany. The youths who are high school dropouts in the United States would, at the age of 14, 15, or 16, have completed normal schooling in almost every other country. They would be serving as apprentices, receiving on-the-job training in industry, or working at entry jobs in factories, retail establishments, or in some service capacity. None of the countries studied considered that these youngsters were unsuitable material for industrial training or employment. On the contrary, employers with whom we spoke said they could find immediate use for U.S. high school dropouts, provided they had no serious mental or physical disabilities. They pointed to the thousands of imported foreign workers who had a much lower average educational attainment, with no apparent effect upon their employability.

Yet, in the United States, dropouts who leave school at about age 16 are often considered unfit for training in industry or even for unskilled jobs. Are these youths so inferior or so poorly prepared for employment as compared with West European youths of the same age and with about the same or, in some cases, even less education? Is our technology so far in advance of that in Western Europe that a high school education is a prerequisite for even entry occupations? Or is the U.S. level of unemployment so high that employers can afford to set qualifications for new workers which are much higher than necessary for available job openings?

Answers to these questions should help us develop policies and programs better suited to solve not only the high school dropout problem, but also to deal with the broader problem of vocational education in the United States.

We believe that the dilemma of the unemployed high school dropout is as much a social as an economic and educational problem. It stems, in part, from a lack of correspondence between the normal terminal point in our precollege educational system and the age at which youths are legally permitted to leave school and seek full-time employment. The social norm in the United States calls for all boys and girls, regardless of interest or ability, to attend school at least until they finish high school, which is usually at age 18. But in most states they may quit school and seek work at age 16. Those who take this route are regarded as having deviated from the norm and are branded as inferior products—high school dropouts—regardless of their reason for leaving school. This is a social stigma which many of them never shake off.

In other countries the dropout problem is virtually unknown because the terminal point in a youth's normal schooling coincides with the age when he either enters the world of work or goes on to special vocational training. He does not have to drop out of anything in midstream, because at 14, 15, or 16 (depending on the country) he has reached a normal stopping point in his education. Prospective employers accept him for what he is, without wondering why he did not finish the years of schooling that every normal boy and girl is expected to complete.

If there is anything in this line of reasoning, we in the United States should try to achieve a coincidence between the normal terminal point in our precollege educational system and the minimum age when youths may accept full-time employment. This can be done either (1) by raising the school-leaving age and, at the same time, changing the curriculum to make school a worthwhile experience for the youths who constitute our present dropout problem; or (2) by reorganizing our educational system to introduce a normal stopping point at age 16 for those who choose not to continue their education. This should not deter the large majority from continuing their schooling to age 18 or beyond. It will, however, erase the social stigma from those who decide to terminate their education earlier.

Either alternative calls for drastic rethinking of our present approach to precollege education. But this is long overdue.

Studies — Volume Breakdown

Studies Prepared for the National Commission on Technology, Automation, and Economic Progress

APPENDIX VOLUME I: *The Outlook for Technological Change and Employment*

Department of Labor, Bureau of Labor Statistics, "America's Industrial and Occupational Manpower Requirements, 1964–75"

George L. Perry, University of Minnesota, "Employment, Output, and Policy Requirements for Full Employment"

Paul Armer, "Computer Aspects of Technological Change, Automation, and Economic Progress"

Merrill Flood, "Commercial Information Processing Networks—Prospects and Problems in Perspective"

Thomas Stout, "Manpower Implications of Process Control Computers in the Process Industries"

Eugene S. Schwartz and Theodore O. Prenting, "Automation in the Fabricating Industries"

Department of Labor, Bureau of Labor Statistics, "Industry Productivity Projections"

APPENDIX VOLUME II: *The Employment Impact of Technological Change*

Department of Labor, Bureau of Labor Statistics, "Disemployment of Labor at the Establishment Level"

Frank Lynn, "An Investigation of the Rate of Development and Diffusion of Technology in our Modern Industrial Society"

Edwin Mansfield, "Technological Change: Measurement, Determinants, and Diffusion"

Walter R. Butcher, "Productivity, Technology, and Employment in U.S. Agriculture"

Joseph P. Newhouse, "Technological Change in Banking"

William Haller, Jr., "Technological Change in Primary Steelmaking in the U.S., 1947–65"

Harold R. Walt, State of California, Department of Finance, "The Four Aerospace Contracts: A Review of the California Experience"

Ronald P. Black and Charles W. Foreman, "Transferability of Research and Development Skills in the Aerospace Industry"

Department of Health, Education and Welfare, Public Health Service, Division of Air Pollution, "Technological Change as it Relates to Air Pollution"

Department of Health, Education and Welfare, Federal Water Pollution Control Administration, "Water Pollution Control"

Department of Health, Education and Welfare, Public Health Service, Division of Environmental Engineering and Food Protection, "Report on the Solid Waste Problem"

Edward W. Hassell, U.S. Department of Commerce, "The Role of Technological Change in Transportation Policy"

James F. Dickson, M.D., "The Life Sciences, Technology, and Unmet Human and Community Needs"

Abt Associates, Inc., "Survey of the State of the Art: Social, Political, and Economic Models and Simulations"

Richard L. Lesher and George J. Howick, "Backgrounds, Guidelines, and Recommendations for Assessing Effective Means of Channeling New Technologies in Promising Directions"

Spectrum Books on Economics

The American Assembly Series

The Classics in History Series